MONOGRAPHS OF THE
AMERICAN SOCIETY OF MAMMALOGISTS

These monographs are a series of publications similar in character to articles published in The Journal of Mammalogy, but not suitable for periodical publication because of their length or for other reasons.

The plans for this Series are broad and comprehensive, and contemplate the publication of works covering all phases of technical and popular mammalogy.

The Monographs and The Journal of Mammalogy are issued under the auspices of the American Society of Mammalogists.

Information regarding these monographs may be obtained from the Secretary of the American Society of Mammalogists, A. Brazier Howell, U. S. National Museum, Washington, D. C., or the Publishers, The Williams & Wilkins Company, Baltimore, U. S. A.

This series is edited by Hartley H. T. Jackson, Bureau of Biological Survey, Washington, D. C.

MONOGRAPHS OF THE
AMERICAN SOCIETY OF MAMMALOGISTS

1. ANATOMY OF THE WOOD RAT. A. Brazier
   Howell, U. S. Biological Survey, Washington, D. C. 225 pages. $5.00.

   In Preparation

2. THE BEAVER. Edward R. Warren, Colorado
   Springs, Colorado.

3. LIFE OF THE CARLSBAD CAVERN. Vernon
   Bailey, Washington, D. C.

   Other titles will be announced.

   Prices are net postpaid

The American Society of Mammalogists participates in the profits from
the sale of monographs. These profits are used to assist in publishing
such monographs that could not be undertaken unless underwritten.

ANATOMY OF THE WOOD RAT

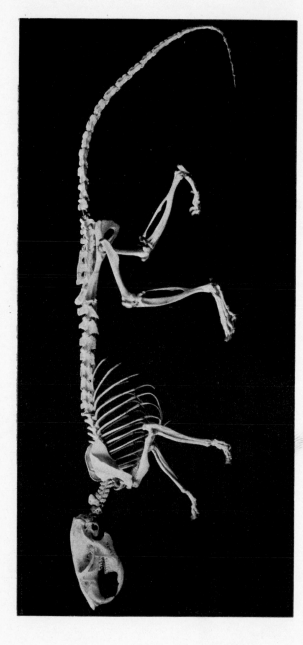

Mounted Skeleton of Male Wood Rat (Type of *Neotoma* (*Homodontomys*) *fuscipes fuscipes*, No. 22026, U. S. National Museum)

MONOGRAPHS OF THE
AMERICAN SOCIETY OF MAMMALOGISTS

NUMBER 1

ANATOMY
of the WOOD RAT

COMPARATIVE ANATOMY OF THE SUBGENERA OF THE AMERICAN WOOD RAT (GENUS NEOTOMA)

BY

A. BRAZIER HOWELL
U. S. Biological Survey

BALTIMORE
THE WILLIAMS & WILKINS COMPANY
1926

CONTENTS

CHAPTER I

CHAPTER II

CHAPTER III

CHAPTER IV

CHAPTER V

CHAPTER VI

CHAPTER VII

CHAPTER VIII

CHAPTER IX

CHAPTER I

INTRODUCTION

The internal anatomy of all but a few mammals has been woefully neglected. Anatomists have heretofore shown a strong propensity to seek out material representing the rarer and more spectacular mammals and to neglect species of a more generalized nature available in abundance. For example, the anatomy of such curiosities as the aye-aye (*Cheiromys*) and the marsupial mole (*Chrysochloris*) is far better known than that of a single one of our more common North American small mammals. Then too, our knowledge of the systematic position of most groups and genera has reached a deadlock, broadly speaking, since cranial and external characters usually employed in their phylogenetic arrangement are mostly well known. Additional work is often productive only of a better arrangement of the species and subspecies within a group or genus. Thus the emplacement of the latter in the system may be largely artificial, and such mistakes as may have occurred can be rectified only after there has been secured a more thorough knowledge of the gross anatomy.

A handicap to the study of the anatomy, especially the myology, of such mammals as rodents is the lack of a comprehensive text book. Even so common a laboratory subject as the white rat has never been thus treated. Existing literature of this nature is either scattered and fragmentary or so poorly illustrated that none but an experienced anatomist can work with it to proper advantage. In addition, the average systematic mammalogist is loath to expend the time and effort necessary to homologize his subject with the

1

anatomy of the cat or of man, which is now necessary if one is to have confidence in his results.

The object in undertaking the present investigation was to gain a comprehensive understanding, from a practical viewpoint, of certain portions of the gross anatomy of a medium-sized, generalized, cricetine rodent. Attention has been paid to correlating the groups of limb muscles and to the effects of their functions and stresses upon the bones of the skeleton. This work was done in order that it might constitute a basis upon which the writer might investigate to better advantage the convergence exhibited by mammals of diverse affinities toward types highly specialized for certain definite modes of life. The present paper constitutes part one of this program. It was made comparative in order that it might be of greater technical value, and that we might learn more regarding the anatomical variation to be expected within those closely-related groups of mammals which we term subgenera. Since illustrations are prerequisite to anatomical work of a satisfactory character, a series of these has been prepared which it is hoped will prove entirely adequate.

It would have been highly desirable to have investigated at least the more critical points in the anatomy of every species and a number of subspecies of the genus *Neotoma*. It is practically certain that a new phylogenetic arrangement considerably better than the one now in use could thus be obtained. It is not unlikely that there exist anatomical differences between some of the more distinct species of the subgenus *Neotoma* that might serve to differentiate these subgenerically. It would take years, however, to secure the material necessary for such an undertaking. It should therefore be emphasized that the present program can not definitely settle the subgeneric standing of the different groups of wood rats. Comparisons are used solely to ascertain and indicate anatomical differences that may be expected to occur between three representative species of their respective subgenera.

It seems hardly necessary to call attention to the fact that this contribution can lay no claim to completeness. During its preparation many problems were encountered, each of which would well repay months of investigation. But a definite program was laid out and followed, and the work is as comprehensive as was deemed necessary for the special purpose for which it was prepared.

For reasons explained hereafter, *Homodontomys* has been arbitrarily selected as the basic type with which to compare first *Neotoma*, and then *Teonoma*.

In the various osteological measurements and percentages, care has been taken to have the individual specimens always follow in the same sequence.

MATERIAL AND ACKNOWLEDGMENTS

The present investigation was made at the U. S. National Museum under the auspices of the Bureau of Biological Survey of the U. S. Department of Agriculture, and the writer is indebted for the use of facilities and material, consisting of a great quantity of skins and skulls, belonging to both of these. It is also a pleasure to acknowledge indebtedness for the securing or loan of material to the Museum of Vertebrate Zoology through its director, Doctor Joseph Grinnell, and to Messrs. Donald R. Dickey and Laurence M. Huey. For advice he is also under obligation to Doctor Ernst Huber of the Johns Hopkins Medical School.

Specimens of superior quality preserved in formalin, representing *Homodontomys* (race *macrotis*) and *Neotoma* (race *albigula*) were collected in surplus quantity either by the writer or under his direction, and three individuals of *Teonoma* (race *cinerea*) by the writer. Upon several occasions subsequent to the start of the investigation individuals of the *Homodontomys* were trapped for special observation of fresh material.

A considerable proportion of the skeletons available were in such condition as to be of limited value for the purposes in hand, although most of them were excellent. The skeletons available consisted of the following:

Skeletons

Neotoma (Homodontomys) fuscipes fuscipes.................... 9
"   "   "   macrotis.................... 1
"   (Neotoma) albigula albigula.......................... 4
"   "   desertorum................................ 2
"   "   floridana rubida........................... 2
"   "   intermedia intermedia..................... 1
"   "   lepida stephensi........................... 2
"   "   pennsylvanica pennsylvanica............... 1
"   (Teonoma) cinerea cinerea........................... 5
"   "   "   occidentalis...................... 1
"   "   "   orolestes......................... 1

ILLUSTRATIONS

Any work on anatomy is well nigh useless without illustrations. In this is it especially true that an illustration may be more illuminating than a dozen pages of text. In such work it is almost imperative that the investigator prepare his own drawings in order to show exactly what he wishes.

It has been the purpose of the writer to illustrate every detail of the portions of the anatomy treated that he considered at all worth while, without carrying this to a useless extreme. An effort has also been made to have the illustrations self-explanatory to as large a degree as possible.

In making the drawings, the writer used a camera lucida while tracing with a pencil the salient features, after which corrections were made, and the figure finished with ink. No effort was made to correct the distortion by the foreshortening inevitable in the use of the camera lucida, and which at times may have been accentuated without realizing it. For this, as well as other reasons, the drawings must be considered semi-diagrammatic. Thus, for clarity, the curved surfaces of the specimen are somewhat flattened in the drawings, so that the same detail of a side muscle is usually shown in both the dorsal and ventral aspect of the subject. Similarly, faint details are intensified—a muscle that may present a paper-thin edge to view is represented as thicker, et cetera.

In the bilaterally symmetrical drawings of muscles which are bisected by a solid line, the detail to the left of the latter is represented as being the more superficial and to the right as deeper.

From the viewpoint of an experienced anatomist, some of the drawings of muscles are shown in too much detail, and a more finished effect would have been obtained by illustrating only muscles of one or two particular groups in each figure. From the standpoint of the systematic mammalogist who may wish to do some slight work in myology, however, it is preferable to illustrate the muscles so as to show their positions in respect to as many of their neighbors as possible.

In those drawings showing muscle attachments upon the bone, blue represents the origins of the muscles and red the insertions. These, too, must be considered as semi-diagrammatic, for many times the insertion of a muscle is tissue-thin, and for distinctness these must always be shown as much thicker; so that distortion in the true positions of the muscles often follows.

Fascial origins and insertions are usually represented as being at the side of, rather than upon, the bone. Finally, attention must be called to the fact that it is often quite impossible to decide the precise limits of a fascial origin or insertion.

In those drawings which are chiefly concerned with the muscles, the names of the latter, abbreviated as little as practicable, are presented in lower case letters, while other terms, as for bones or glands, are printed in capital letters.

In the myological drawings the intermuscular penetration and emergence of some of the chief nerves is shown, these being represented as cut.

CHAPTER II

SYSTEMATIC POSITION OF NEOTOMA AND ITS SUBGENERA

Under current usage the genus *Neotoma*, as segregated by Say and Ord in 1825, is one of the six genera included in the subfamily Neotominae, of the family Cricetidae. Perhaps the majority of authorities consider this subfamily to be most nearly related to the subfamily Microtinae, chiefly because of the enamel pattern of the molariform teeth. This is a rather logical contention, but on the other hand, it is not unlikely that the tooth pattern is fortuitous in this respect, having been brought about by certain food habits, and that the similarity of the pattern in the two subfamilies is not of great phylogenetic significance.

The generic diagnosis as given by Goldman (1910) is as follows: "Molar crowns flat; first and second upper molars with middle enamel loops undivided; third lower molar with two transverse enamel loops (not S-shaped as in all other genera of the subfamily); bullae oblique, tapering anteriorly."

The subgenus *Teonoma* was proposed by Gray in 1843, and *Homodontomys* by Goldman in 1910.

The key to the three subgenera, as given by Goldman, is as follows:

a. Tail terete, not bushy.
  b. Maxillary tooth row much narrower posteriorly than anteriorly; middle lobe of last upper molar not divided by inner reentrant angle....................*Neotoma*
  b'. Maxillary tooth row slightly narrower posteriorly than anteriorly; middle lobe of last upper molar partially or completely divided by inner reentrant angle........*Homodontomys*
a'. Tail flattened and bushy....................................*Teonoma*

6

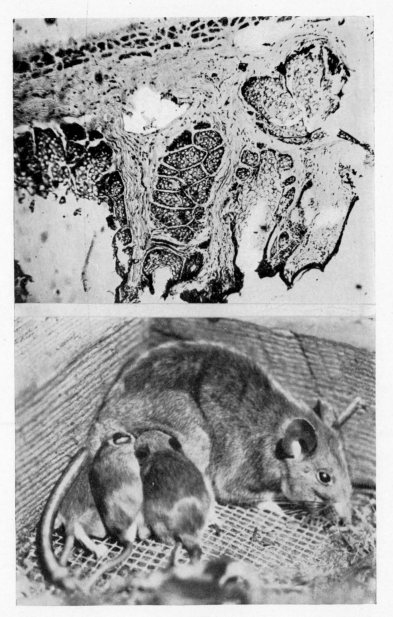

PLATE 2

Upper: Section (much enlarged) through the ventral dermal gland of male *Teonoma cinerea*, showing specialized sebaceous glands for secreting the scent characteristic of these animals.

Lower: A captive female wood rat (*Homodontomys*) with three young attached to nipples.   Photo. by P. F. English.

Within the subgenus *Neotoma* Goldman recognized seven groups. Of it there have been accepted, at least tentatively, 26 species and 35 subspecies out of the total of 72 forms so far proposed (see Miller, 1924). The subgenus *Homodontomys* includes but one well-marked species, of which there are considered to be five valid subspecies, while five additional forms described have been placed in synonymy. The subgenus *Teonoma* is also considered to contain but a single species, of which there are eight subspecies, with five more placed in synonymy. There have thus been 97 forms of the genus *Neotoma* described.

The range of the genus extends from the Atlantic to the Pacific, but is discontinuous in much of the eastern United States; and from Nicaragua north in British Columbia almost to Alaska.

CHAPTER III

HABITS OF THE THREE SUBGENERA STUDIED

The habits of *Neotoma* are generalized to a very large degree. Apparently this wood rat can not adapt itself to semi-aquatic surroundings as can the Norway rat (*Rattus norvegicus*), nor is it ever found in a strictly prairie habitat. It does occur, however, from the very hottest part of the country below sea level to above timberline, and from portions of the desert with meager growth to the densest forests of the northwest. It may be found miles from any tree worthy of the name, or living among the branches high overhead. It is at home in an underground burrow at the base of a cactus, in the attic of a deserted building, or among the crannies of a boreal cliff. Activity is almost wholly confined to the hours of darkness, although occasionally the animals may be observed abroad during daylight.

The life habits of a species often vary to a considerable extent with locality, depending upon variation in the environment, to which individuals must largely fit themselves. Habits as here set forth apply only to the localities with which the author is familiar.

Neotoma (*Homodontomys*) *fuscipes macrotis* Thomas is an animal of the Upper Sonoran and Transition zones, but it extends also into the Canadian. A typical environment is the side of a canyon, among scattered live oaks and high brush. Here it may build a large nest of sticks, it may supplement this with subterranean burrows, may live in the decayed heart of a large oak, or where trees are numerous, it frequently constructs nests of respectable size high among the branches. If a nest be kicked to pieces the occupant often seeks escape by climbing a nearby tree and

8

running through the branches, and I have shot many specimens in such situations. Certainly this subgenus exhibits tendencies which are more arboreal than those of any other wood rat within the United States.

The food staple of this animal under the above conditions seems to be seeds, pinyon nuts and acorns, shrub seeds and berries in season. It is also known that another subspecies is very partial to certain fungi (see Parks, 1922). It probably indulges in considerable insect food, and meat when available; but when necessary it can supplement a dwindling larder with more bulky items, such as bark or fibrous roots. Its fare, in fact, is probably as concentrated as a rodent of its type could be expected to be.

Neotoma (Neotoma) albigula albigula Hartley is one of a well-defined group of its subgenus. It is a resident of the Upper and Lower Sonoran zones of the Arizona, New Mexico and northern Mexico desert areas. It may be found in any situation where subsoil moisture conditions favor a moderate growth of shrubby plants and scattered trees, such as the borders of a "wash" of a foothill canyon. It usually builds a nest of respectable dimensions, or it may occupy a cranny in a rocky outcrop. I have known it to seek safety in the hollow trunk of a tree, but never among the upper branches. It may be presumed to climb thither, however, in search of such berries as the elder.

The chief food item of this form is also seeds and berries. It often gnaws cacti, undoubtedly for the moisture content, and for the same reason, may be presumed to consume any succulent vegetation available. Due to the climatic exigencies of its environment it seems probable that this animal is obliged to consume a greater proportion of roughage, from time to time, than is *Homodontomys*; but this is largely conjecture.

Neotoma (Teonoma) cinerea cinerea (Ord), with its subspecies, is the "pack rat" of the western mountains. At least two of its races normally live as low as the Upper Sonoran zone; but the subgenus is essentially boreal in its predilections. The subspecies *cinerea* is usually found amid the park-like country of the high mountains, where it frequents rock slides. It may also be found wherever there is cover of a comparable character, as in abandoned buildings.

Deep among the rocks it has its nest of sticks and trash, and even when there is no other evidence from above, the location of its home is often advertised by the characteristic odor of the animal. During favorable seasons individuals may fairly swarm in certain slides, while there is no sign of them in others apparently as suitable. From the slides the vicinage is scoured for suitable food during the hours of darkness. Where they occur the snowfall is usually heavy, and it is believed that they are active throughout the winter. Hence they must accumulate some sort of food supply. They too are partial to seeds and nuts, but throughout most of their range chipmunks (*Eutamias*) fairly swarm, and these, being more active and wide-ranging as well, secure most of the harvest. *Teonoma* must therefore rely to a great extent upon less concentrated fodder, and I have found it feeding on the stems of grasses and the bark of alders. Invariably the stomachs of the scores of individuals examined have been crammed with herbaceous matter, which imparted a tinge of green to the entire alimentary tract. It is believed that this character of food constitutes by far the largest proportion of the total consumed by this subgenus.

These animals are adept at climbing rocks and the intricacies of old buildings, and doubtless they would be equally at home among the tree tops. It is not believed that they indulge in tree climbing, however, except rarely for some special fruit.

PLATE 3

WOOD RAT (*Homodontomys*) IN THE BRANCHES OF A TREE

Photo. by P. F. English

CHAPTER IV
EXTERNAL FEATURES

Measurements and weights

Neotoma is a rodent of rat-like form and size; but there is much variation within the genus as regards the latter character. Body length varies from 150 mm. in the case of *Neotoma lepida*, to as much as 238 in some races of *Teonoma*, although selected males of *Homodontomys* (as *fuscipes*) having longer tails seem to surpass all other wood rats in total length.

Neotoma (Neotoma) albigula albigula. Averages of the collector's measurements in millimeters for a series of fifteen adult topotypes secured by the writer and now in the collection of D. R. Dickey, are as follows: For eight males: length of head and body, 194 (169–209); tail, 144 (125–165); hind foot, 33.6 (32–37). For seven females: length of head and body, 186 (167–203); tail 144 (123–153); hind foot, 33.7 (33–34). A specimen typical of those used for dissection weighed in the flesh 182 grams, while after it had been preserved in spirits and allowed to drain for five minutes, its weight was 235 grams. Hence, this specimen had soaked up moisture to the extent of nearly 30 per cent of its original weight. The others may be presumed to have done the same in like proportion.

Neotoma (Homodontomys) fuscipes macrotis. Averages of the collectors' measurements for a series of sixteen adult topotypes in the collection of the Biological Survey are as follows. For eight males: length of head and body, 190.6 (170–209); tail, 177 (170–195); hind foot, 38 (35–40). For eight females: length of head and body, 183 (160–200); tail, 170 (160–175); hind foot, 37.4 (35–38). A spirit

11

specimen typical of those used for dissection weighed 307 grams, after being allowed to drain for five minutes.

Neotoma (Teonoma) cinerea cinerea. Averages of the collectors' measurements for a series of twelve adults from various portions of the Sierra Nevada in California are as follows. For six males: length of head and body, 222 (210–234); tail, 176 (164–185); hind foot, 45.5 (42–49). For six females; length of head and body, 218 (208–229); tail, 165 (158–179); hind foot 43 (41–45). A specimen, unusually large but typical of the three used for dissection, weighed 395 grams after having drained for five minutes.

From the above averages it is apparent that the females are consistently smaller than the males in length of head and body. This measurement of the females constitutes the following percentages of the same measurement for males: for *Homodontomys*, 96; *Neotoma*, 95.5; and *Teonoma*, 98.2. In consideration of the fact that long tails are especially subject to accidental shortening during life, the slight sexual difference in the length of this member as indicated may or may not be trustworthy. The sexual difference in the length of the hind foot is insignificant except for *Teonoma*, in which the foot of the female is 94.5 per cent that of the male.

It will be seen that for head and body length of males, *Neotoma* is 87.4 per cent of *Teonoma*, and *Homodontomys* is 85.8 per cent of the same animal. This probably indicates to a fair degree of accuracy the true difference in body measurement of the three species considered. Having no real connection with this is a comparison of the body weights of three of the specimens, representing the three subgenera, which were dissected. The figures are illustrative only of the differences in the cubic capacity, and hence mass, of the three series available, and are not considered to be representative of the true relational differences as found in animals of like age and development. The weight in grams of the specimen of *Neotoma* was 59 per cent of that of *Teonoma*, while the weight of the *Homodontomys* was 78 per cent of the same animal.

It is found that in striking an average of both males and females, the length of tail as taken in the flesh is 93 per cent of the head and body in *Homodontomys*, 76 per cent in *Neotoma*, and 77.5 per cent in *Teonoma*.

Although there are many exceptions, probably caused by some inhibiting factor or compensating character in the com-

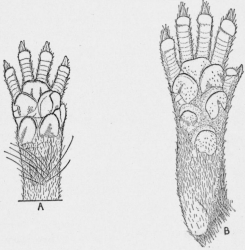

Fig. 1. Palmar and plantar aspects of (A) fore and (B) hind feet of *Teonoma*, showing plan of pads, and carpal vibrissal area.

position of certain mammals, it may be stated as a rule that arboreal specialization in a mammal accompanies either lengthening of the tail or an increase in the length of hair upon the sides of that member (*e.g.*, many squirrels). This is an arboreal specialization, but variation in this respect is found in mammals that are not truly arboreal. Thus, within certain groups of rodents, those (other than saltatorial forms) which dwell amid a plains environment have the shortest tails (*Lagurus, Citellus beldingi*, certain hamsters, etc). Mammals living among tall grass or brush that is not dense have tails slightly longer for their respective groups (*Microtus townsendi, Peromyscus m. sonoriensis*, etc.). Rodents frequenting moderately heavy brush usually have tails that are slightly longer still (*Microtus mordax*, which frequents situations more brushy than do most voles; *Peromyscus b. rowleyi*, etc.), while mammals of the heaviest brush or forests, which may also be partly arboreal, have the longest tails (*Peromyscus m. oreas, Neotoma (Homodontomys) fuscipes*).

Thus, *Neotoma albigula* has the shortest tail of any of the three subgenera studied, which undoubtedly means that this member has not been used to as great an extent as a balancer while the animal was climbing into and among bushes and trees. *Homodontomys* has much the longest tail of the three, indicating that it is consistently used as a balancer while its owner is clambering about in precarious situations. . The tail of *Teonoma* is negligibly longer than that of *Neotoma albigula*, but in the former this member is heavily clothed with long hairs, and it is known that this character answers the same purpose as greater length. Theoretically it may be accepted that the hairy tail of *Teonoma* is of as much aid to its owner in negotiating the rocks and cliffs of its habitat as is the long, terete tail of *Homodontomys*. Whether in practice it is actually more efficient in such situations or less so we shall probably never know.

There is some variation in the relative size of the hind foot of the three species. In *Homodontomys* this member is 20.2 per cent of the length of the head and body; in *Neotoma* it is 17.7 per cent; and in *Teonoma*, 20.4 per cent. This is also in accordance with the line of reasoning offered in the case of the tail. The hind foot of *Neotoma*, which is the most generalized of the three, is relatively shortest, and the toes are also shorter and narrower. In *Homodontomys*, living in heavy brush and to some extent in trees, the foot is definitely longer, with the toes long and slender. *Teonoma*, spending much of its life climbing among the rocks, has a foot proportionately the same length as the last, but the feet and toes are much heavier and broader. The same conditions are found in the fore feet of the three animals.

Appendageous and integumentary characters

The moderately dense hair upon the sole of the pes extends in appreciable amount only as far forward as the rearmost pad. This hair is most scanty in *Homodontomys* and is dark sooty; in *Neotoma* it is slightly more abundant and white in color; while although still short, it is in much greater abundance in *Teonoma*, and of a buffy shade. There is an anterior and a posterior central pad or tubercle, while four others are situated two mediad and two laterad, one pair in front of the other, making six pads in all. There are five toes, the hallux being small as usual, while the other four are larger and well formed, and all five are furnished with claws.

The manus is also moderately hairy as far forward as the rear pad. Of the latter there are two mediad and two craniad, one pair in front of the other, and craniad to this is a central anterior pad. There are four well formed digits furnished with nails, but the pollex is rudimentary and without a nail—a mere nubbin upon the side of the foot.

The region of the external nares is not peculiar, and the rhinarium is of the typical murid form. As might be expected, the parts are more heavily haired in *Teonoma*. The labio-nasal sulcus of the upper lip is moderate, but can not be considered as well developed.

There is so little actual disparity in the size of the ear in the three subgenera that it is impossible to draw any conclusions regarding the slight relative differences existing. The length of ear, measured from the notch, is in *Homo-*

dontomys 27.5 mm.; *Neotoma* 28 mm.; and *Teonoma* 29 mm. The width of ear, given in the same order, is 22.5, 22, and 25 mm. Hairiness of this member shows individual variation, and variation with age as well. In *Teonoma* the ears of juveniles especially are better haired than in adults. Hairiness of ear is moderate in all cases, but in old individuals of *Homodontomys* and *Neotoma* this member may be practically naked. There is usually a slight covering composed of very fine buffy hairs along the helix, and a sprinkling of slightly darker hairs upon the terminal third or two-fifths of the pinna. The antitragus is double and

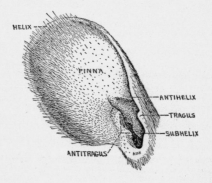

FIG. 2. Details of external ear of *Homodontomys*

but slightly indicated (fig. 2), nor is the tragus strongly formed. The subhelix consists of a light cartilaginous fold well within the conch, and the antihelix takes the form of a low ridge. Variation in the form of the ear between the three subgenera is not appreciable.

In all females of the genus *Neotoma* there are two pairs of inguinal teats, located close together and somewhat suggestive of the mammae of a young heifer.

Ventral dermal gland. As previously mentioned the males of *Teonoma* exhibit a thickened dermal area midventrally which may have a width of 70 mm. and a breadth of 35 mm.

In females this portion of the integument is barely thicker than over the remainder of the animal, and seems to be without marked glandular action. Microscopical examination of vertical sections of this area shows many enlarged, highly specialized glandular masses of the sebaceous type (see plate 2). Some are engorged with secretion, and appear as though this were accompanied by a progressive breaking down of the more ental cells. They are separated by trabeculae, carrying the secretion to the external surface. It can not be doubted that these highly specialized sebaceous glands act as scent glands, which is perfectly apparent even to human faculties. There are no suderiferous glands in any of the sections examined.

PELAGE

The body, in the genus *Neotoma*, is covered with hairs of moderate length, without underfur, coloration is of the type termed agouti in various shades of brown, and the hairs of the upper surface are plumbeous at base. In *Homodontomys* the hairs of the dorsal and lateral portions of the body attain a length of about 15 mm., but in addition there is a small proportion of overhairs, or "guard" hairs, black tipped and with a length of about 20 mm. The hairs upon the head are considerably shorter, in all subgenera. Upon the lateral borders of the ventral surface, the hairs, now shorter, still have plumbeous bases, but the tips are buffy. Midventrally the hairs are buffy white, clear to the bases, except for an area roughly 40 mm. in length, located centrally upon the midventral line of males where the hairs are considerably coarser and of a dirty brownish color. The integument of this area is slightly thicker than upon the remainder of the belly, and there is undoubtedly increased glandular action of the skin at this point. A characteristic of this subgenus is the sootiness of the dorsum of the manus and of the pes. The tail is the same shade above and below, and is covered with short hairs of a dark, sooty shade.

Neotoma albigula is of a paler, more buffy color than *Homodontomys*, and some of the guard hairs, slightly scantier, are buffy instead of blackish. The latter attain a length of only about 14 mm., while the denser body hairs average about 11 mm. The sides are inclined to be more buffy, with fewer dark hairs, and there is an abrupt line of demarcation between these and the white hairs with plumbeous bases of the ventral surface. There is a narrow zone of hairs along the midventral line which are white to the base, and the pelage of the inguinal and axillary regions, and of the throat and chest, are similar. Especially in males there is often a naked area about 40 mm. long and 5 wide upon the central portion of the midventral line, coarser in texture and more scaly than the remainder of the integument. The hairs upon the dorsum of the feet are pure white. The tail is rather sharply bicolor, sooty above and white below, and is covered with hairs that are slightly longer than in *Homodontomys*.

The coloration of the adult *Teonoma* is more variable than of the others, varying from a brighter tawny shade to tones of gray. It being an animal of more strictly boreal predilections, its pelage, even in summer, is considerably longer. The body hairs are softer than in the other subgenera, and are slightly the longest about the shoulders, where they reach a length of about 22 mm. The long, black, guard hairs, about as numerous as in *Homodontomys*, may reach a length of 27 mm. There is an abrupt transition of color pattern upon the sides to the white of the ventral surface. The hairs of the lateral portions of the latter are plumbeous at base, but for a width of about 30 mm. along the midventral line they are entirely white. In males the hair of the midventral region of the belly is much coarser over an area about 70 mm. long and 35 in width and show a strong buffy discoloration. Beneath this the integument is much thickened, forming a glandular area (see p. 16). In females this portion of the integument is slightly thickened, but there is no discoloration nor coarsening of the hairs, and this feature enables one to distinguish between adults of the two sexes at a glance. The hairs upon the dorsum of the foot are white. The tail is bicolor, white below and somewhat sooty, or "pepper and salt" above. The hairs are dense and of equal length upon all sides of the tail, and may attain a length of 10 mm. near the base and 30 mm. upon the remainder of the tail; but they grow in such manner that they lie close to the member upon its dorsal and ventral surfaces, and are spread laterally, so that the tail is somewhat "feathered," inclining in this manner toward the condition obtaining in many arboreal mammals. That this is not an exceedingly ancient specialization is probably indicated by the fact that in juveniles a quarter grown this lateral feathering of the tail is only just appreciable and the appendage is densely covered with hairs no longer than 9 mm.

In all instances juveniles of the genus *Neotoma* are plumbeous in color, as is the case in most rodents of rat- or mouse-like type.

An examination of large embryos and newly born young, as well as of adults, discloses the fact that there are no areas over which the hair is inclined craniad or in other direction save caudad upon the body, and distad upon the limbs.

Vibrissae. The mystacial vibrissae of the buccal region[1] vary considerably in length, and those measuring in excess of 30 mm. vary in number from 16 to 25. In *Homodontomys* they may reach a length of 80 mm. and are black. In *Neotoma* they have white tips, but are usually black at base and grow as long as 65 mm. In *Teonoma* some are black at base with white tips, and others solid white, and they may reach 100 mm. in length. Each grows from a subcutaneous, tactile papilla springing from the tough, fibrous tissue beneath the integument of the upper lip and is served

[1] For vibrissal terminology see Pocock, 1914.

by one of the numerous branches of the infraorbital nerve, which is of large size in the present genus. It can not be doubted that these vibrissae are highly sensitive and play an important rôle in the economy of the animal. It may be presumed that the longer vibrissae of *Teonoma* have been developed to serve as a better tactile organ in the dark intricacies of the rock slides which are frequented by that animal.

Anterior to the longer mystacial vibrissae are a number of short ones of varying length, usually white in color. Upon

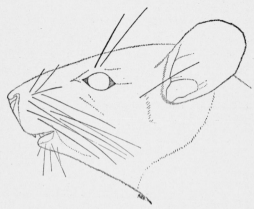

Fig. 3. Details of cephalic vibrissal areas of *Homodontomys*, and showing relative proportion of ear to head.

the chin are a number of hairs, but slightly coarser than and twice as long as the surrounding pelage, which should be considered as submental vibrissae; but they can have but slight function and are probably decadent.

The superciliary vibrissae (fig. 3), situated above the eye, are usually two in number, but often only one, occasionally three, and in a specimen of *Homodontomys*, five. They may be as short as 21 mm. in *Neotoma*, or as long as 30 mm. in *Homodontomys*, and 45 mm. in *Teonoma*.

The vibrissa which seems to correspond with the area which Pocock terms the genal, but in the present animal situated between the ear and the eye, apparently never exceeds one in number. Its usual length is 20 mm. in *Neotoma*, and 40 in *Homodontomys* and *Teonoma*.

In a single individual dissected—a *Homodontomys*—there was one vibrissa growing from a tactile papilla upon the interramal area, caudad of the region of the symphysis menti. In no other was this encountered, nor could it be demonstrated in any of the numerous study skins upon which I have searched for it.

Situated on the caudo-ventral aspect of the distal forearm, immediately above the wrist, are the carpal vibrissae (fig. 1). These, too, grow from subcutaneous, tactile papillae, are about 12 mm. in length, and vary from three to nine in number. The minimum was encountered in *Neotoma* and the maximum in *Teonoma*; but there seems to be more individual than subgeneric variation in this respect. It is extremely likely that they are tactile in character.

CHAPTER V

MYOLOGY

PREFATORY NOTE

In works on anatomy it is usual to have the osteological portion precede the myological, but in the present instance so much information on the muscles is included with the descriptions of the bones that for the sake of convenience the chapter on myology is placed first.

It is, perhaps, unfortunate that no two works on myology have ever employed the same arrangement of the muscles, but this is inevitable with our present state of ignorance regarding the group relationship of many muscles. To assemble them by regions, save in the broadest sense, is misleading and meaningless. As group relationship of the muscles is established by their innervation one must arrange them with this constantly in mind. It is always found, however, that no inflexible rule can be followed, and any arrangement now used must be largely theoretical and idealistic. In the present instance the arrangement employed takes into consideration the probable basic grouping of the muscles of mammals in general—not of the wood rat in particular. This, at first glance, may not seem to conform to the functional grouping presented on page 185 but closer attention will show that practically it does. The more purely phylogenetic arrangement can not be strictly logical in all instances, however. For instance, the M. quadriceps surae is placed with the flexors of the lower leg, although the soleus does not act as such but only as an extensor of the foot.

The neurology of the genus *Neotoma* was investigated only to the extent necessary to establish the innervation of

practically all the muscles save the smaller ones of the
feet. When the nerve constituted a smaller branch of a
plexus, however, the intricacies of the latter were not
always followed.

In working out the myology of *Neotoma* only those muscles
readily distinguishable have been included, and the micro-
scopic examination of many specimens to establish the
presence or absence of doubtful fibers was at no time considered. In the case of a number of vestigeal muscles it is
often extremely difficult to differentiate the few fibers
present from the tougher connective tissue (for instance, in
the manus), and different investigators would arrive at
varying conclusions. Hence, it was considered better to
adopt a conservative attitude and recognize only those
muscles regarding the presence of which there could be no
reasonable doubt.

Myological dissections were made of three specimens of
each species of the three subgenera, so as to have a check
on those details which exhibit a tendency to vary. In
addition, certain muscles of a variable character and certain
nerves were investigated in additional specimens of both
Neotoma and *Homodontomys*. An examination was also
made of special features of *Neotoma intermedia*, *N. micropus*,
and *N. floridana rubida*.

In each case, the muscles of *Neotoma* (*Homodontomys*)
fuscipes macrotis are the ones described in the text, and
remarks are made upon the corresponding muscles of the
subgenera *Neotoma* and *Teonoma* only when these differ to an
appreciable extent. This course was followed solely because
specimens of *Homodontomys* happened to be available in
greater quantity. As the work progressed it was found
that from an anatomical standpoint this procedure happened to be the most desirable one.

It is perhaps unnecessary to call attention to the fact
that the musculature of no two specimens is precisely the

same. There are minute differences that may be, and undoubtedly are, phylogenetic in character; there are analogous, ontogenetic differences caused by the fact that the life led by various individuals causes variation in the muscular development; and finally, no two specimens ever "set" in precisely the same position after having been placed in preservative.

It should also be noted that in many instances it is impossible to define the exact bounds of the attachment of a muscle. This is especially the case when a muscle ends in fascia. In addition, difficulties in deciding whether or not certain differences are relative are presented when an unusually large *Teonoma* is compared with a subadult *Neotoma* of much smaller size.

Myological terminology is in a fairly satisfactory state of standardization as regards human anatomy, but this is far from so in the case of the lower mammals. Hence, until an authoritative revision of the nomenclature with special reference to the lower Mammalia has been made, no standard can be attained. Many of the usual muscle names are misleading when applied to such a mammal as the wood rat, but the coining of new terms by the individual investigator is to be deplored, and the only practical course to follow in most cases seems to be the employment of such names, established by usage, as appear best to fit the subject in hand.

MUSCLES OF THE HEAD

The muscles of the head are treated under the following headings:

Superficial facial musculature
Masticatory musculature
Interramal musculature
Muscles of the tongue

I. Superficial facial musculature

The superficial facial musculature is poorly defined in the present genus, especially in *Homodontomys* and *Neotoma*. A microscopical study would bring out more of it, but after a careful, gross examination, only nine of these muscles were considered to be sufficiently well defined for inclusion in the present work. These are as follows:

Mm. platysma   auriculo labialis
      interscutularis   levator labii
      orbicularis oculi   dilator naris
      orbicularis oris   sternofascialis
      buccinatorius

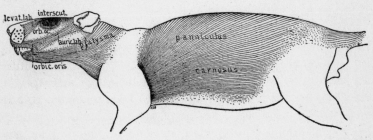

FIG. 4. Superficial facial musculature and panniculus carnosus of *Teonoma*.

M. platysma (fig. 4) may be considered as arising by two heads. The more dorsal originates from the middorsal line, extending from the occiput to the interscapular fossa. It passes latero-craniad over the side of the neck and joins the ventral head. The latter originates from the midventral line near the manubrium and extends craniad to fusion with the other head. Cranially the muscle merges with the orbicularis oris upon the chin.

In *Neotoma* this muscle is not so well defined, but in *Teonoma* it is slightly more so, and stouter.

M. interscutularis (fig. 4). Fibers which correspond to this muscle are lightly indicated. They extend across the fore part of the cranium between the ears and eyes, and merge partially with fibers of the orbicularis oculi and auriculo labialis.

M. orbicularis oculi (figs. 4, 23, 24) originates from the frontal bone immediately mediad of the lachrymal, and is poorly developed. Its fibers surround the eye, and some of them merge with those of both the interscutularis and levator labii.

M. orbicularis oris (fig. 4) is with difficulty separable from the tough tissue about the lips, especially in *Homodontomys*, and is rather poorly developed in the genus.

M. buccinatorius (figs. 5, 23, 24). This thin sheet of muscle has origin from the portion of the premaxilla and maxilla along the curve formed by the root of the incisor from near its alveolus almost to the infraorbital foramen directly ventrad to the origin of the infraorbital slip of the masseter. Passing ventrad, the fibers upon its superficial belly develop noticeably into striated fat cells, and the rest of the muscle passes insensibly into the mucous membrane of the cheek, and thus to the orbicularis oris. A small portion of the muscle, similarly inserted, also has connection with the tissue overlying the diastema of the mandible. This muscle is often classed with the masticatory group, but in rodents it plays but little part in actual mastication.

M. auriculo labialis (zygomaticus) (fig. 4) is a slender band of muscle extending from the orbicularis oris, at the corner of the mouth, across the cheek, with insertion at the base of the cartilage of the ear. A few of the dorsal fibers may be continuous with the interscutularis.

M. levator labii (figs. 4, 23, 24) is well defined, especially in *Neotoma*. Origin is along the lateral margin of the ascending branch of the premaxilla for some 7 mm., extending cranio-ventrad in a fan-wise manner to an insertion upon the fibrous, mystacial pad.

M. dilator naris (figs. 5, 23, 24) lies deep to, and is

entirely covered by, the levator labii. It is a very slender muscle arising from a slight fossa upon the dorsal part of the zygomatic process of the maxilla. It quickly becomes tendinous and is inserted upon the lateral side of the anterior nasal opening.

M. sternofascialis (fig. 7) occurs in *Homodontomys* only as a slender slip arising from the midventral line at the posterior end of the manubrium. It extends caudo-dorsad beneath the platysma and disappears in the fascia covering the parotid gland. It constitutes a remnant of what is often called the deep panniculus, or in certain mammals, the sphincter colli profundus.

In neither *Neotoma* nor *Teonoma* could a trace of this muscle be found.

The innervation of the superficial facial musculature is by the N. facialis.

II. Masticatory musculature

In rodents the chief muscles of mastication are divisible in varying degree, but they had best be treated as occurring as parts of four, main muscles, as follows:

Mm. masseter	pterygoideus externus
temporalis	pterygoideus internus

In addition, the digastric is an important masticatory muscle in most if not all rodents, but this had best be placed elsewhere.

M. masseter is divisible, with more or less ease, into three main parts, comprising the following:

Pars **superficialis** (figs. 5, 7, 23, 24, 25), having origin by a heavy tendon from the slight process immediately cranio-ventrad to the infraorbital foramen. The tendon broadens to form a tough aponeurosis covering all the lateral belly of the muscle excepting its extreme posterior portion. The muscle fibers take origin chiefly from the ental surface of this aponeurosis. Insertion is upon both the lateral and medial surfaces of the ventral border of the angular process.

In *Neotoma* this division is a trifle broader in its anterior portion. In *Teonoma* the cranial border extends slightly farther forward, and the insertional portion extends farther mediad.

Pars **zygomaticus** (figs. 5, 6, 7, 23, 24, 25) whose deeper cranial borders blend somewhat with the adjoining ones

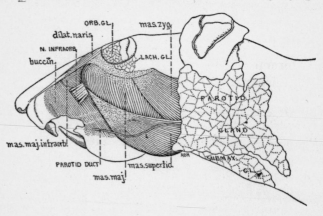

FIG. 5. Head of *Homodontomys*, showing the more superficial glands and certain muscles. (Ear cartilage cut.)

of the next part (major), have origin from the ventro-lateral border of that portion of the zygomatic arch which lies caudad to the masseter major. It is inserted upon the whole of the angular process of the mandible save its extreme ventral border.

Pars **major** (figs. 5, 6, 7, 23, 24, 25) arises by three heads—the (*a*) ectal, (*b*) ental and (*c*) infraorbital.

(*a*) The ectal head arises upon the superior portion of the septum and anterior border of the maxillary root of the zygomatic arch, extending caudad to within a couple of millimeters of the jugal. Insertion is upon the masseteric ridge of the mandible.

(*b*) The ental head has origin from the orbital surface of the septum of the maxillary root of the zygoma and the inner border of the arch. It develops an aponeurosis upon its ental belly, to which are attached the fibers of the infraorbital head as well as a few from the temporalis, and the narrow insertion is mainly in a line extending from the anterior termination of the masseteric ridge to the base of the mandibular condyle.

(*c*) The infraorbital head has origin from the infraorbital fossa, and passing caudad through the infraorbital foramen, descends and is inserted upon the medial surface of the aponeurosis of the ental head.

M. temporalis (figs. 6, 23, 24, 25) is imperfectly divisible into two portions, least well developed in *Homodontomys*, slightly better in *Neotoma*, and best in *Teonoma*. The more superficial and anterior part arises from the temporal ridge almost as far caudad as the interparietal. The posterior border is very thin, and to a slight extent aponeurotic. Some of the ental fibers are inserted upon the superficial surface of the aponeurotic sheet covering the deep division, making the two difficult to separate at this point. Passing within the orbit, it is inserted upon the ental surface of the coronoid process of the mandible and its root, and also upon the aponeurosis descending from the ental division of the masseter major.

The posterior or deep part of the temporal arises from that portion of the temporal ridge and fossa immediately laterad of the interparietal, from the lambdoidal crest and the part of the temporal fossa cranio-ventrad thereto. The ventro-lateral portion bulges well over the zygomatic process of the squamosal but it is not attached at this point. As it descends craniad, a superficial aponeurosis develops, which converges to a tendinous insertion upon the tip of the mandibular coronoid process and a small part of the ectal surface adjoining.

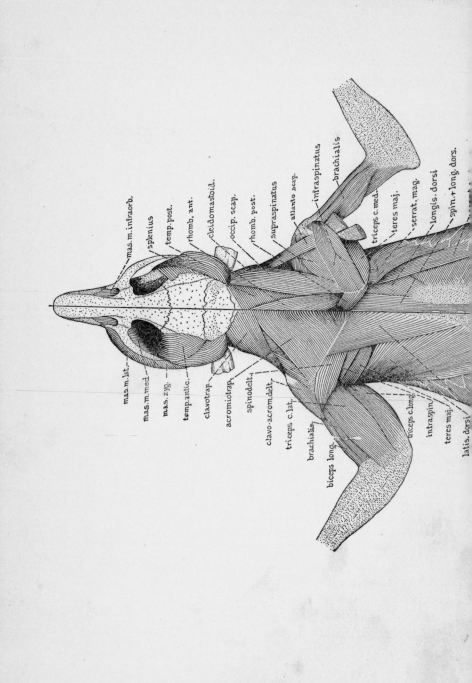

mas.m.infraorb.
splenius
temp.post.
rhomb, ant.
cleidomastoid.
occip. scap.
rhomb. post.
supraspinatus
atlanto scap.
infraspinatus
brachialis
triceps c. med.
teres maj.
serrat. mag.
longis. dorsi
spin.+ long. dors.

mas.m.lat.
mas.m.med.
mas. zyg.
temp.antic.
clavotrap.
acromiotrap.
spinodelt.
clavo-acromdelt.
triceps c.lat.
brachialis
biceps long.
triceps c.long.
intraspin.
teres maj.
latis.dorsi

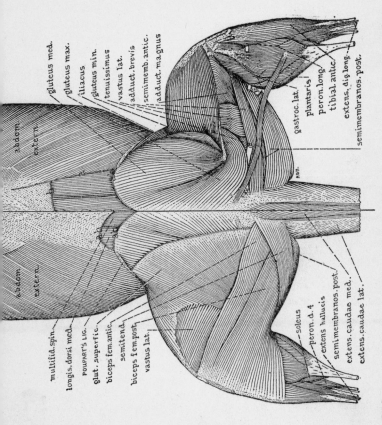

multifid. spin.
longis. dorsi med.
POUPART'S LIG.
glut. superfic.
biceps fem.antic.
semitend.
biceps fem. post.
vastus lat.

gluteus med.
gluteus max.
iliacus
gluteus min.
tenuissimus
vastus lat.
adduct. brevis
semimemb. antic.
adduct. magnus

abdom.
extern.

abdom.
extern.

nat.

soleus
peron. d. 4
extens hallucis
semimembranos. post.
extens. caudae med.
extens. caudae lat.

gastroc. lat.
plantaris
peron. long.
tibial antic.
extens. dig. long.
semimembranos. post.

Fig. 6. Dorsal musculature of *Homodontomys:* superficial layer upon left,
much of the next deeper layer to the right (*a*, superficial; and *b*,
deeper lumbo-dorsal fascia, cut)

M. pterygoideus externus (figs. 23, 24) has origin from the ectal surface of the parapterygoid plate, with insertion upon the medial face of the mandibular condyle.

M. pterygoideus internus (figs. 8, 23, 24) originates from the pterygoid fossa, and insertion is onto practically the whole of the medial face of the angular process of the mandible.

The innervation of these four muscles of mastication is by the N. trigeminus.

III. Interramal musculature

Of these there are four, as follows:

Mm. digastricus   transmandibularis
    stylohyoideus   mylohyoideus

M. digastricus (figs. 7, 23, 24, 25) has origin from the paroccipital process. Passing craniad it becomes largely but not entirely tendinous at a point laterad to the hyoid. There is here tendinous attachment to the raphe of the mylohyoid. Craniad to this point the muscle once more broadens, becoming entirely fleshy, and is inserted upon the ventral border of the mandible caudad to the symphysis menti. There is little difference in size between the posterior and anterior bellies.

In *Neotoma* the anterior belly is considerably broader than the posterior and the tendinous constriction between them is more sharply defined and more tendinous. In *Teonoma* the anterior belly is much larger than the posterior, and larger than in *Homodontomys*, completely hiding the transversus mandibularis. The tendinous constriction between the bellies is larger and more muscular.

As previously mentioned, there would be some grounds for placing this muscle with the masticatory group, but its innervation is different. The anterior belly is served by a branch of the inferior alveolar nerve, and the posterior by the N. facialis.

M. stylohyoideus (figs. 7, 8, 23, 24) has origin from the base of the paroccipital process deep to the origin of the digastric. Insertion is upon the greater cornu of the hyoid. In *Homodontomys* this muscle is hardly larger than the posterior termination of the hyoglossus, while in *Teonoma* it is at least twice the mass, extending more antero-laterad and being more strongly inserted upon both the cranial and caudal borders of the cornu. In *Neotoma* it is intermediate in development.

Innervation is apparently by the N. facialis.

M. transversus mandibularis (figs. 7, 24) is an unpaired muscle connecting the two mandibular borders just caudad to the symphysis menti. It has attachment upon either side in rather illy-defined fossae.

M. mylohyoideus (figs. 7, 24) has origin from the medial surface of the ramus of the mandible, extending from near the root of the first molar to a point just caudad of the root of the last molar. Insertion is with its fellow into the medial raphe, and onto the cranial border of the hyoid bone.

This muscle and the transversus mandibularis are both served by the inferior alveolar nerve.

IV. Muscles of the tongue

This group, as here defined, is composed of

Mm. styloglossus   genioglossus
hyoglossus

M. styloglossus (figs. 8, 23, 24). The origin of this slender muscle should apparently be considered as from the slight process upon the infero-posterior margin of the auditory meatus rather than from the mastoid, as is usually stated to be the case in rodents. Extending forward immediately entad to the ramus of the mandible, insertion is into the tongue through the cranio-lateral portion of its base.

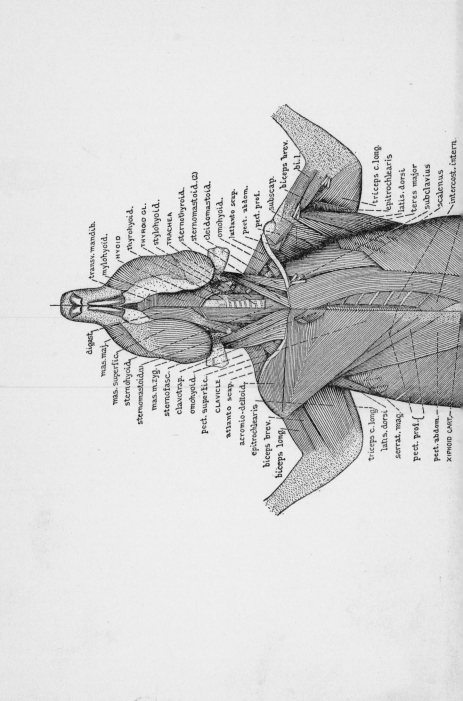

transv. mandib.
mylohyoid.
HYOID
thyrohyoid.
THYROID GL.
stylohyoid.
TRACHEA
sternothyroid.
sternomastoid. (2)
cleidomastoid.
omohyoid.
atlanto scap.
pect. abdom.
pect. prof.
subscap.
biceps brev.
bi. l
triceps c. long.
epitrochlearis
latis. dorsi
teres major
subclavius
scalenus
intercost. intern.

digast.
mas. maj.
mas. superfic.
sternohyoid.
sternomastoideu.
mas. m. zyg.
sternofasc.
clavotrap.
omohyoid.
pect. superfic.
CLAVICLE
atlanto scap.
acromio-deltoid.
epitrochlearis
biceps brev.
biceps long.
triceps c. long!
latis. dorsi
serrat. mag.
pect. prof.
pect. abdom.
XIPHOID CART.

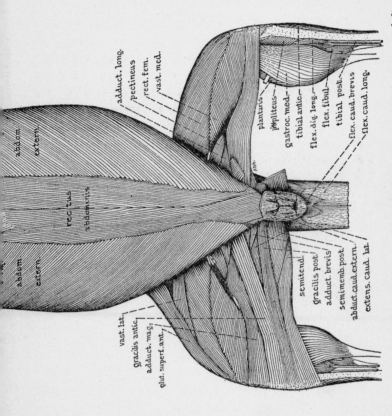

abdom extern.

rectus abdominus

abdom extern.

adduct. long.
pectineus
rect. fem.
vast. med.

vast. lat.
gracilis antic.
adduct. mag.
glut. superf. ant.

plantaris
popliteus
gastroc. med.
tibial. antic.
flex. dig. long.
flex. fibul.
tibial. post.
flex. caud. brevis
flex. caud. long.

semitend.
gracilis post.
adduct. brevis
semimemb. post.
abduct. caud. extern.
extens. caud. lat.

Fig. 7. Ventral musculature of *Homodontomys*: superficial layer upon left, with much of next deeper layer to the right

M. hyoglossus (fig. 8) has origin along the anterior
border of the entire hyoid, including the greater cornu and
the body. Near the origin it is in contact with its fellow
of the opposite side, but it at once diverges, passing cranio-
laterad deep to the styloglossus, and is inserted upon the
lateral margin of all but the anterior portion of the base
of the tongue.

M. genioglossus (figs. 8, 24). The more anterior and
superficial part of this muscle, especially in *Teonoma*, is
partially divisible into two, parallel portions, between which
passes a branch of the hypoglossal nerve. It has a relatively weak origin from the symphysis, and at the other
extreme, is definitely attached to the hyoid, deep to the
last. Closely pressed to and partly integral with its
antimere, it constitutes the medial portion of the tongue.

The innervation of these three tongue muscles is by the
N. hypoglossus.

MUSCLES OF THE BODY

The muscles of the body are gathered under the following
headings:

I. Muscles of the neck
II. Muscles of the trunk

I. MUSCLES OF THE NECK

The muscles of the neck are again divided into

1. Superficial group
2. Supra- and infrahyoid group
3. Deep lateral and subvertebral group

1. SUPERFICIAL GROUP

These are but two in number, as follows:

Mm. sternomastoideus
cleidomastoideus

M. sternomastoideus (figs. 7, 23, 24) is usually perfectly separable into two divisions in the case of *Homodontomys*. The more superficial of these arises from half the cranial border of the manubrium: the deeper one arises similarly, deep to the first. Both are inserted, mostly by tendon fibers, onto the mastoid process of the squamosal.

In *Neotoma* the muscle is usually inseparable except at the insertional end, and is slightly broader and heavier. In *Teonoma* it seems to be really separable at no point, and is also slightly larger than in *Homodontomys*.

M. cleidomastoideus (figs. 6, 7, 23, 24, 29) has a tendinous origin from the mastoid process of the squamosal, with insertion upon the clavicle deep to the clavotrapezius. In *Teonoma* this muscle is somewhat broader and coarser.

Both of the foregoing muscles are served by the N. accessorius.

2. SUPRA- AND INFRAHYOID GROUP

Under this heading belong

Mm. omohyoideus   thyrohyoideus
  sternohyoideus   geniohyoideus
  sternothyroideus

M. omohyoideus (figs. 7, 8, 28) is very thin and fragile, but comparatively broad, and arises from the basal portion of the suprascapular notch. It passes superficial to the sternothyroid, partly between the digastric and the sternohyoid, and is inserted deep to the insertion of the latter muscle upon the hyoid bone.

In *Neotoma* and *Teonoma* this muscle is much thicker and better defined.

M. sternohyoideus (fig. 7) is the chief muscle lying immediately ventrad of the trachea. Origin is from the first costal cartilage. Passing craniad adjacent to its fellow of the opposite side, insertion is onto the body of the hyoid bone.

M. sternothyroideus (figs. 7, 8) is a slender muscle lying laterad of the trachea and deep to the sternohyoid. Its origin is upon the sternum beneath the sternohyoid and it is inserted upon the thyroid cartilage.

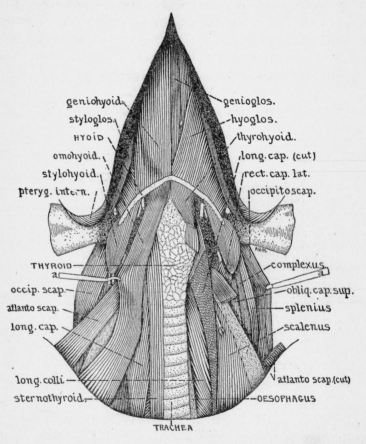

FIG. 8. Throat and interramal musculature of *Teonoma:* more superficial muscles at left, deeper on right. (*a* representing wire hooks.)

The innervation of the omohyoid, sternohyoid and sternothyroid is by the ansa hypoglossi.

M. thyrohyoideus (figs. 7, 8) is a small, short muscle

arising from the hyoid, and it is inserted upon the thyroid
cartilage. At first glance this might be mistaken for an
anterior extension of the sternothyroid, as it is of about the
same width as that muscle.

M. geniohyoideus (figs. 8, 24) lies deep to the mylohyoid and close to its fellow along the medial line. Origin
is from the medial surface of the mandibular ramus just
caudad to the symphysis. The fibers run caudad and are
inserted onto the cranial border of the hyoid deep to the
insertion of the mylohyoid.

Innervation of these two muscles is by means of the
hypoglossal nerve.

3. DEEP LATERAL AND SUBVERTEBRAL GROUP

Under this heading belong the

| Mm. scalenus | longus capitis |
| longus colli | rectus capitis anterior |

M. scalenus (figs. 7, 8, 9). This, with some difficulty,
is divisible into three parts. The portion corresponding
to the scalenus anticus arises from the first rib about where
this joins its cartilage, and is inserted upon the transverse
processes of several of the cervical vertebrae.

The medial division lying superficial to the original
portion of the levator scapulae has origin from the third
and fourth ribs. Extending craniad from beneath the
caudal slip of the levator scapulae, insertion is by muscle
fibers and investing aponeurosis chiefly upon the atlas, but
to a slight extent upon the transverse processes of most if
not all of the remaining cervical vertebrae as well.

In *Neotoma*, origin is from the fourth and fifth ribs,
while in *Teonoma*, it is from the fifth and sixth.

The third and most ventral division of the scalenus
has origin by slips from the third, fourth and fifth ribs.
These at once unite and the resulting muscle band emerges

from the cranial border of the obliquus abdominis externus, extending partly superficial to the medial division of the scalenus. It passes into four slender tendons which are tucked in, each succeedingly deep to the preceding, and inserted upon the transverse processes of the first four cervical vertebrae, that to the atlas being slightly the largest. In a single specimen the portion of the origin from the third rib seemed to be lacking.

In both *Neotoma* and *Teonoma* origin is from the fourth and fifth ribs only.

M. longus colli (figs. 8, 10) lies in contact with its antimere between the oesophagus and the cervical vertebrae. It is a muscle complicated in its attachments, which are exceedingly difficult to follow with precision. Suffice it to say that the thoracic portion arises from the bodies of several of the thoracic vertebrae, the insertion being for the most part upon the ventral branch of the transverse process of the sixth cervical vertebra, especially modified in so many mammals. The cervical portion, being merely a continuation of the last, arises from the transverse processes and centra of the cervical vertebrae, and the fibers, converging cranio-mediad, are inserted upon the tubercle upon the ventral arch of the atlas. In *Teonoma* the cranial portion is larger and better defined.

M. longus capitis (figs. 8, 23) has origin from the transverse processes of the middle five cervical vertebrae. Insertion is upon the anterior portion of the basioccipital. In *Teonoma* origin seems to include the seventh vertebra as well.

M. rectus capitis anterior (fig. 23) is a small muscle easily overlooked. It extends from the atlas to the basioccipital just caudad of the longus capitis.

All muscles of this group are innervated by branches of the cervical nerves, but these were not followed with exactitude.

II. MUSCLES OF THE TRUNK

The muscles of the trunk may be divided into

A. Muscles of the thorax
B. Muscles of the abdomen
C. Lumbar muscles
D. Muscles of the back
E. Muscles of the tail
F. Perineal musculature

A. Muscles of the thorax

As here segregated, these number eleven, as follows:

Mm. panniculus carnosus
 pectoralis superficialis
 pectoralis profundus posterior
 pectoralis profundus anterior
 pectoralis abdominalis
 subclavius

serratus magnus
levator scapulae
intercostales externi
intercostales interni
sternocostalis

M. panniculus carnosus (figs. 4, 29). Origin of this muscle should, perhaps, be considered as non-integral with the latissimus dorsi. Connection is continuous with the latter, but in reality origin is largely tendinous and just mediad to the biceps. The muscle diverges from the axillary fossa with strongly developed fibers, joining its fellow of the opposite side upon the midventral line at a point slightly craniad to the xiphoid process of the sternum, and upon the middorsal line at a point immediately dorsad of the axillary fossa. The fibers disappear in the fascia covering the posterior half of the belly, the groins and the gluteal region, and the lower back. Fibers again develop, however, at the base of the tail. The muscle is strongest near its origin and in its cranio-dorsal portion. Caudad it is difficult to decide just where the fibers cease.

In *Neotoma* the panniculus is somewhat better developed —stronger and more extensive—and the main portion reaches well onto the base of the tail. In *Teonoma* it is very similar to that in *Homodontomys*, although the fibers hardly meet upon the midventral line or extend so far upon the belly; but they occur slightly more caudad in the gluteal region.

As is usual the pectoral mass is divisible into four portions. The names here applied to them are only tentative, for the precise homology of the pectoral muscles in the lower mammals can be established only after extended investigation.

M. pectoralis superficialis (figs. 7, 29). This portion takes origin along the midventral line from the manubrium to the last sternebra—a distance of 25 mm. The anterior portion is to some extent bipennated, and the muscle is with some difficulty separable along this line. The cranial border skirts a portion of the clavicle, and the whole converges to an insertion partly by muscle and partly by tendon fibers upon the deltoid crest of the humerus and its proximal ridge, partly deep to the deltoid, for a distance of some 12 mm.

In *Neotoma* the origin is considerably longer (33 mm.), while in *Teonoma* the muscle is a trifle thicker as well, with origin 31 mm. in length. In both these subgenera this division entirely hides the pectoralis profundus anterior.

M. pectoralis profundus posterior (figs. 7, 29). The origin of this slender portion is from the caudal part of the xiphoid process. It at first follows the caudal border of the profundus anterior, and the aponeurotic insertion is upon the deltoid crest and ridge of the humerus deep to that of the superficial division.

In *Neotoma* this is separable from the profundus anterior only with difficulty. In *Teonoma* it is slightly broader, with the cranial border entirely hidden beneath the superficial pectoral.

M. pectoralis profundus anterior (figs. 7, 29) has origin from all the sternebrae (but not the manubrium)

and the cranial portion of the xiphoid, practically the
entire muscle lying deep to the superficial pectoral. Insertion is by aponeurosis along the deltoid ridge, the base
of the greater tuberosity, and upon the extreme lateral end
of the clavicle.

M. pectoralis abdominalis (figs. 7, 29) corresponds to
what is sometimes called the xiphihumeralis. It has
origin upon the midventral line from a trifle craniad of the
posterior termination of the profundus posterior caudad for
a distance of 18 mm.; thence by fascia, origin extends

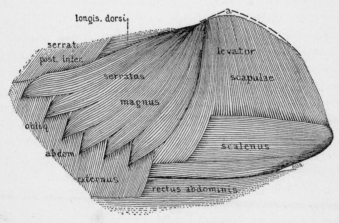

FIG. 9. Subscapular and thoracic musculature on right side of *Teonoma*,
with scapula removed (*a* showing position of scapular border).

directly laterad as far as the abdominal external oblique.
This muscle is at first ribbon-like but soon contracts, becoming triangular in cross section, and is inserted upon the
head of the humerus mediad of the insertion of the profundus anterior division.

In *Neotoma* it is not so well developed, the insertional
end especially being weak. In *Teonoma* it is more sharply
triangular.

M. subclavius (figs. 7, 29) is the only portion of the

sternoscapularis present. It is a short, slender muscle which is easily overlooked, arising from the cartilage of the first rib, and is inserted upon the distal end of the clavicle.

M. serratus magnus (figs. 6, 7, 9, 29). The fibers upon the cranial border of this muscle are separable from the levator scapulae only with difficulty, but as the origin is distinct, the insertion fairly so, and the innervation of the two is not the same, there is no reason why they should not be considered as constituting separate muscles. Origin is by fleshy digitations from the cranial border of five ribs— the fifth to ninth inclusive. Insertion is by muscle and tendon fibers upon the caudal portion of the vertebral border of the scapula, and this is twisted upon itself in characteristic fashion.

In *Teonoma* this muscle is similar except that origin is from six ribs—the sixth to eleventh inclusive.

M. levator scapulae (figs. 9, 29). This hardly seems the proper place for this muscle, and an attempt was first made to treat it as a division of the serratus, but such is not possible, for its innervation is different from that of the serratus, and it was found to be a specialized levator scapulae, as termed in most works on the lower mammals. A better name for it would really be depressor scapulae, as that is its present function brought about by the change in the relational position of the shoulder due to the posture of the animal; but it was thought wiser to retain the usual term. It has origin from the transverse processes of the last five cervical vertebrae and the first four ribs. The original portion of the muscle is about 25 mm. in width. Most of it emerges dorsad from beneath the dorsal border of the scalenus; but the portion arising from the fourth rib constitutes, in reality, a separate head, for it progresses dorsad from its origin for several millimeters between the bellies of the two longer divisions of the scalenus before

emerging superficial to that muscle and joining the remainder of the levator at the dorsal border of the scalenus.
In *Homodontomys* the emergence from the scalenus is at a
point about midway between the dorsal and ventral borders
of the latter. The muscle converges to a fleshy insertion
along the medio-dorsal border of the scapula between the
insertions of the rhomboidii and serratus magnus.

Neotoma is very similar, except that the caudal slip
emerges ectad of the scalenus well towards the dorsal
border of the latter. In *Teonoma* the original width is
about 30 mm., the increase of five millimeters compensating
for the fact that it arises from the first *five* ribs, and it
emerges from the scalenus considerably nearer its ventral
border.

The innervation of this muscle is from the cervical
plexus—not from the brachial plexus as would be the case
were it a part of the serratus.

Mm. intercostales externi (fig. 10). The external intercostals join each rib to its neighbor. The fibers have
a tendency to extend cranio-dorsad, though this is hardly
true in the case of the more caudal series. Until after the
seventh rib is passed they do not extend between the costal
cartilages, but only between the true ribs. After that the
external intercostals occur between the cartilages as well.
The fibers passing cranio-dorsad from the more dorsal
part of the third rib are not inserted upon the second, but
extend farther craniad and are inserted upon the first rib.

Mm. intercostales interni (figs. 7, 10). These are
situated chiefly deep to the last, to which they are similar
except that the fibers have a tendency to pass cranio-
ventrad. Without removing the external intercostals
they are to be seen only where they join the first seven
costal cartilages one with another.

In *Teonoma* the diaphragm is placed farther craniad
than in the other two subgenera, being undoubtedly so

forced by the greater mass of the alimentary tract and the liver. It presents no peculiarities in this genus. The central semilunar tendon is extensive and into this are radially inserted the fibers of the

M. sternocostalis, which take origin by muscular bundles interdigitating with the transversalis from the xiphoid process and the sixth to twelfth ribs. In *Neotoma* origin from the twelfth rib is doubtful, and in *Teonoma* origin is not only from the twelfth rib, but the thirteenth as well. No other sternocostal muscle was differentiated.

The two crura are located upon the middorsal line of the body cavity, arising upon either side. Origin is from the first and second lumbar vertebrae, and passing craniad, each is inserted fanwise upon the dorsal portion of the semilunar tendon. In *Teonoma* origin seems to be from the first four lumbar vertebrae.

The innervation of all these muscles, save the levator scapulae as already mentioned, is by way of the brachial plexus, all of whose branches were not followed in precise detail.

B. *Muscles of the abdomen*

The five muscles of the abdomen are

Mm. rectus abdominis   transversalis
    obliquus abdominis externus   cremaster
    obliquus abdominis internus

M. rectus abdominis (figs. 7, 9, 10, 11B, 32). By virtue of its attachments, a better name for this muscle would be rectus thoraco-abdominalis, but the more usual term is employed. It has origin from the pubis just laterad of the symphysis by two slips which decussate with those of the opposite side (fig. 11B). In *Homodontomys* it was found that the more ventral slip of the right side extended superficial to that of the left, and similarly with the deeper divisions. The superficial slip of the right muscle was

narrower than that of the left. The two slips of either
muscle join immediately craniad of the decussation and the
single muscle thus formed upon either side passes in contact with the midventral line or linea alba to the xiphoid
cartilage, at which point it diverges slightly from the midventral line to its insertion upon the first costal cartilage,
and to a slight extent, the manubrium. In a total of four
specimens of *Homodontomys* in which this muscle was investigated the decussation of the right muscle was found
invariably to be superficial to the left, but it is not unlikely that there is some individual variation in this respect, as in the other subgenera. The tendency for the
divergence of the rectus from the midventral line in the
thoracic region was found to be greatest in *Homodontomys*
and least in *Teonoma,* with *Neotoma* intermediate in this
respect.

In *Neotoma* decussation of the left muscle was found to
be superficial to the right in two specimens, and the reverse
in one. In all three the more superficial slip was only about
half as wide as the one beneath it. In *Teonoma* the decussation of the left muscle was also found to be superficial
to the right in two specimens and the reverse in one. In a
single instance the more superficial slip was less than half
the width of the one beneath it, but both were of approximately equal width in the other two.

The three muscles covering the side of the abdomen,
which at some points are separable only with extreme
difficulty, comprise the following.

M. obliquus abdominis externus (figs. 6, 7, 9) has
origin by slips from the last nine ribs interdigitating with
those of the serratus magnus as far as this extends, and
from the ectal surface of the lumbodorsal fascia. Insertion is for the most part upon the sheath of the rectus
abdominis just mediad to the lateral margin of that muscle,
and upon Poupart's ligament. The latter extends from

the inferior tuberosity of the ischium just caudad of the symphysis to the anterior crest of the ilium, and to it are attached the three muscles of the abdominal wall.

In *Neotoma* and *Teonoma* origin is from the last ten ribs, beginning at the fourth instead of the fifth.

M. obliquus abdominis internus (fig. 10) has origin from the ental surface of the lumbodorsal fascia, but the anterior portion is not clearly separable from the serratus posterior inferior. Origin is also from Poupart's ligament. Insertion is onto the caudal border of the posterior costal

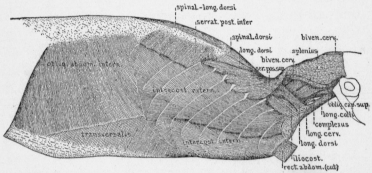

Fig. 10. Deeper muscles of the trunk and neck of *Homodontomys*

cartilages and onto the fascia covering the transversalis some distance dorso-laterad of the rectus abdominis. The ventral portion of the muscle is separable from the transversalis only with so much difficulty that the fibers of the internal oblique present the appearance of being inserted directly upon the deeper muscle.

M. transversalis (figs. 7, 10) has origin from the medial border of those costal cartilages caudad to the diaphragm, and from some of the fibers of the latter, as well as from the fascia deep to the internal oblique. Insertion is upon the aponeurotic sheet investing the ental surface of the rectus abdominis and upon Poupart's ligament.

M. cremaster is present only in the male, and its situation is largely scrotal. In reality it is a development from the internal oblique, and its fibers are to be found between the laminae ectalis and entalis of the tunica vaginalis.

The innervation of the cremaster is by means of the genito-femoral nerve, and of the remaining abdominal muscles, by branches of the lower thoracic nerves; but these were not followed in the present instance.

C. Lumbar muscle

Under this heading there is but a single muscle—the **M. quadratus lumborum** (figs. 12, 33), which occurs in four separate bundles. The first arises from the ninth thoracic vertebra and is inserted upon the diapophysis of the second lumbar vertebra. The others occur similarly save that the last has insertion upon the cranio-ventral border of the spine of the ilium.

This muscle is served by branches from the lumbar nerves.

D. Muscles of the back

The muscles of the back are placed in two divisions—the

1. Superficial, secondary back muscles
2. Deep, intrinsic back muscles

1. SUPERFICIAL, SECONDARY BACK MUSCLES

This more superficial group is further divisible into three layers.

First layer consists of four muscles, which are

Mm. clavotrapezius spinotrapezius
acromiotrapezius latissimus dorsi

M. clavotrapezius (figs. 6, 7, 23, 24, 28, 29) has origin which is continuous with that of the acromiotrapezius along the occipital angle of the cranium extending from just dorsad of the mastoid to the middorsal line, and thence for some 7 mm. caudad. Passing ventrad over the side of the neck and fore chest, insertion is onto the clavicle laterad of the sternomastoid.

In *Teonoma* this muscle seems to be more definitely triangular in shape and the origin does not usually extend so far caudad along the middorsal line, thus forming a narrow hiatus between this and the acromiotrapezius.

M. acromiotrapezius (figs. 6, 28) has origin along the middorsal line from the clavotrapezius to the spinotrapezius for a distance of about 15 mm. Anteriorly it is continuous with the former but the margins quickly diverge and it continues to its insertion upon the cranial border of practically the entire spine of the scapula, and upon the small tendon extending dorsad therefrom.

In *Neotoma* the origin does not quite meet that of the spinotrapezius. In *Teonoma* the origin begins farther craniad and is thus slightly longer. Instead of a tendon extending dorsad from the spine there is a stout fascia running cranio-dorsad.

M. spinotrapezius (figs. 6, 28) has origin from the middorsal line, extending from the posterior part of the origin of the acromiotrapezius caudad, the more caudal portion being from the dorsal fascia. Total origin is about 40 mm. in length. Extending ventro-craniad, insertion is upon the scapular spinal tendon and upon the dorsal third of the spine.

In both *Neotoma* and *Teonoma* the muscle is relatively somewhat weaker.

The trapezius muscles are innervated by the accessory nerve, and it is likely that they also receive small branches from the cervical plexus, although this was not demonstrated.

M. latissimus dorsi (figs. 6, 7, 13, 29) has origin for about 20 mm. upon the middorsal line, beginning at a point directly medio-dorsad of the spine of the scapula.

Thence the origin is from the dorsal fascia for some 25 mm. additional. Passing to the axillary region it converges to a stout tendon (not in common with the teres major) which is inserted upon the lateral spine of the humerus. From the ventro-distal portion of the latissimus arises the epitrochlearis.

In *Teonoma* origin extends for about 5 mm. longer, with the ventral portion of the belly correspondingly broader.

The innervation of this muscle is by a branch from the brachial plexus—undoubtedly the thoraco-dorsal nerve.

Second layer of the superficial, secondary, back muscles includes the

Mm. rhomboideus anticus	occipitoscapularis
rhomboideus posticus	atlantoscapularis

M. rhomboideus anticus (figs. 6, 29). While the posterior rhomboid corresponds to a considerable degree with the rhomboideus major of human anatomy, it is the smaller division in *Neotoma*. The portion here termed anticus is much the larger, and in its attachments does not so closely resemble the usual rhomboideus minor. Hence, terms indicating position seem to be more applicable in the present instance. It has origin from the middorsal line extending from the spine of the axis to the first thoracic vertebra. The muscle converges somewhat, passes along the medio-dorsal border of the scapula and is inserted by both muscle and tendon fibers beneath the insertion of the rhomboideus posticus. This insertion extends to a point at right angles to the border and mediad of the spine.

In *Neotoma* insertion extends hardly at all upon the scapular border but rather it is practically confined to an area upon the scapula at right angles to the border and opposite the spine. In *Teonoma* the cranial portion is narrower and weaker, but the more caudal part of the origin is stronger, being practically continuous with, and

hardly separable from, the origin of the rhomboideus posticus. The insertion, however, is quite distinct, and the
part at right angles to the scapular border is stronger and
more extensive.

M. rhomboideus posticus (figs. 6, 28, 29) has origin
chiefly from the greatly developed spine of the second thoracic vertebra. Insertion is for about 8 mm. along the
dorsal border of the scapula, from the insertion of the
levator scapulae to 3 mm. craniad of the scapular spine.
The ental fibers of this muscle are not so readily separable
from the rhomboideus anticus.

M. occipitoscapularis (rhomboideus capitis or levator
scapulae dorsalis) (figs. 6, 8, 24, 28) has origin for a distance
of 10 mm. along the lambdoidal portion of the cranium
dorso-mediad from the mastoid process of the squamosal.
Insertion is upon both the dorsal border of the scapula
cranially adjacent to that of the rhomboideus anticus, and
upon the extreme dorsal portion of the scapular spine.

These three foregoing muscles are served by nerve
branches from the brachial plexus.

M. atlantoscapularis (figs. 6, 7, 8, 28). This muscle
is usually termed the levator claviculae or levator scapulae
ventralis, but atlantoscapularis is preferable. It is a rather
slender muscle having origin from the ventral arch of the
atlas, with an insertion that is chiefly aponeurotic upon the
border of the metacromion.

The innervation of this muscle is by a branch of the
third cervical nerve.

Third layer of the superficial, secondary back muscles is
made up of the

Mm. serratus posterior superior
serratus posterior inferior

M. serratus posterior superior (figs. 6, 10). There
is some individual variation in the origin of this muscle,

which is by fleshy slips from five of the ribs—the fourth or fifth to the eighth or ninth. Rapidly converging, insertion is by rather weak aponeurosis upon the medial raphe just over the spine of the second thoracic vertebra and partially superficial to the extreme caudal portion of the splenius.

In *Neotoma* origin seems always to begin at the fourth rib and apparently does not extend beyond the seventh. The muscle is so exceedingly thin in this subgenus that its exact bounds are difficult of definition. In *Teonoma* origin is from the fourth to tenth (inclusive) ribs, but very few fibers come from the tenth. Insertion is weaker than in *Homodontomys*, the medial fibers ceasing before the raphe is reached.

M. serratus posterior inferior (figs. 9, 10) has origin from the last five ribs, with insertion upon the lumbodorsal fascia.

It may be noted that the apparent affiliation of this muscle with the serratus posterior superior is slight, and that in practice, the division between it and the obliquus abdominis internus is not to be distinguished with certainty.

The innervation of these two muscles is by the intercostal nerves.

2. DEEP, INTRINSIC BACK MUSCLES

These are divisible into the

| Mm. splenius
long system | transverso-spino-occipital system
deep, short system |

M. splenius (figs. 6, 8, 10, 24). This muscle lies deep to the rhomboideus anticus and occipitoscapularis. As a whole it has origin from the deepest part of the nuchal ligament, extending from the great spine of the second thoracic vertebra to within 10 mm. of the occiput. Insertion is upon the caudal border of the lambdoidal crest and ventro-laterad to the mastoid process of the squamosal. Careful examination discloses the fact that in reality the lateral 3 or 4 mm. constitutes a separate slip, the origin of which is hardly to be separated from the main belly, but with a distinct insertion, by aponeurosis, beneath the lateral portion of the larger mass. It should be noted that this is the deepest muscle arising from the nuchal ligament.

In *Neotoma* the whole muscle is slightly more robust. In *Teonoma* the origin extends closer to the occiput, and the lateral slip is even better differentiated.

This muscle is served by branches of the cervical and probably the thoracic nerves as well.

The long system, or sacrospinal musculature of the back, is most conveniently divided into the

Mm. iliocostales   spinalis dorsi
       longissimus dorsi

M. iliocostales (figs. 10, 11) lie upon the dorsal side of the ribs laterad to the longissimus dorsi. The bundles extend craniad from the eleventh rib, with origin in groups of fibers and small tendons from this to the third (inclusive) rib. Each group is inserted (apparently) upon the fourth rib craniad of its origin, but there is no attachment to the second rib. The muscle as a whole is inserted by tendon fibers upon the first rib and the transverse processes of the sixth and seventh cervical vertebrae.

In *Teonoma* origin begins at the tenth rib, and the muscle is free from the third rib as well as the second.

M. longissimus dorsi (figs. 6, 9, 10, 11, 12, 32, 33). The several subdivisions of this muscle are not very well differentiated in the present animal. *Pars* **cervicis,** often obscure but here separable into a distinct muscle, is figured as the **longissimus cervicis.** It is situated between the thoracico-lumbar portion of the same muscle and biventer cervicis, with origin from the transverse

processes of the first four or five thoracic vertebrae. Insertion is by tendon and muscle fibers onto the transverse
processes of the last five cervicals.

Towards its thoracic end the main portion, constituting
pars **thoracis** of the longissimus, has origin chiefly from
the transverse processes of the thoracic vertebrae. The
lumbodorsal fascia passes deep within the anterior portion,
chiefly in the vicinity of the ninth rib, and gradually
ceases. Insertion is by tendinous fibers upon the transverse processes of the fourth and fifth cervical vertebrae.

The postcostal or lumbar portion, forming *pars* **lumborum**
of the longissimus, is divisible in a sagittal direction as
follows: (*a*) **lateralis** is entered by the deeper lumbodorsal fascia, the fibers originating from both the ectal
and ental surfaces; origin of the extreme caudal fibers is,
however, from the cranial and medial portions of the
anterior ilium; insertion is onto the di- and anapophyses
of the lumbar vertebrae; (*b*) **medialis** has origin from
the spinous processes and metapophyses of the lumbar
vertebrae. Some of the fibers are bipennated onto an
aponeurotic tendon, and insertion is onto the diapophyses
of the vertebrae. The muscle is continuous caudad with
the extensor caudae lateralis.

M. spinalis dorsi (figs. 6, 10, 11) occurs between the
thoracic spines and the longissimus. The more superficial fibers arise directly from the lumbodorsal fascia at
about the ninth rib. The deep part gradually becomes
differentiated from the medial portion of the longissimus,
though not with any degree of clarity until the seventh
rib is reached. The medial fibers interconnect the spinous
processes of the vertebrae craniad to include the spine of
the axis, passing caudad from the spines craniad to the
ninth thoracic, and craniad from those caudad of the
eleventh thoracic.

Various branches, not followed, of the costal nerves
serve this long system.

The transverso-spino-occipital system of the deep back musculature is composed of three muscles—the

Mm. biventer cervicis   multifidis spinae
      complexus

The first two of these in the present animal constitute separate divisions of what is often termed the semispinalis capitis.

M. biventer cervicis (figs. 10, 11, 24). Like so many other muscles of the vertebral column, this one shows considerable individual variation in its attachments, which fact, however, is probably of no practical significance to us. In addition, it is well to mention that this is one of the muscles concerning whose exact limits of extent it is extremely difficult to feel certain.

The caudal portion arises by two heads. The more posterior has origin from the third and fourth to sixth or seventh (inclusive) thoracic vertebrae, while the anterior slip arises from the vertebrae extending from the third thoracic to the axis. Passing craniad, the anterior slip develops an aponeurosis upon its ectal belly and upon the superficial surface of this the posterior slip is inserted. The aponeurosis is, in turn, inserted upon the superior angle of the occiput from its center to the slight tuberosity at its ventro-lateral termination.

In *Teonoma* the posterior slip arises from the fourth or fifth to seventh or eighth thoracic vertebrae, and the anterior one, from the fifth thoracic to the fourth (or sometimes third) cervical vertebra. It is slightly more robust in this subgenus, and the junction of the two slips occurs at a point somewhat more caudad.

M. complexus (figs. 8, 10, 11, 23, 24). Origin of this muscle, between the longissimus cervicis and biventer cervicis, is from the last three cervical and possibly the first thoracic vertebrae. It converges craniad and the tendinous insertion is upon the mastoid process of the squamosal. In *Teonoma* origin is from the last cervical and first two thoracic vertebrae.

M. multifidis spinae (figs. 6, 12). The fibers of this muscle, lying between the longissimus dorsi medialis and the middorsum, have origin from the diapophyses, and

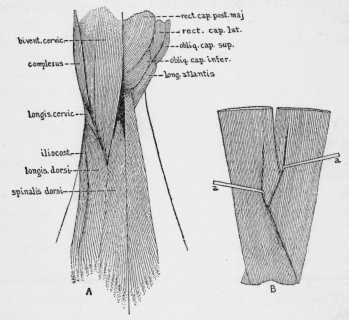

Fig. 11. *A*, Deeper, supravertebral muscles of the cervical region of *Homodontomys:* more superficial upon the left, deepest to right.

B, Decussation of caudal termination of the rectus abdominis muscles of *Homodontomys*. (*a*, representing wire hooks.)

insertion upon the bases of the spinous processes, of the second vertebrae craniad of the origin. The caudal portion of this muscle is known as the extensor caudae medialis. No deeper division was differentiated.

The innervation of these three muscles is by branches of the spinal nerves.

The deep short system of the deep back musculature is composed of seven muscles as follows:

Mm. transversospinales
   rectus capitis posterior major
   rectus capitis posterior minor
   rectus capitis lateralis

obliquus capitis superior
obliquus capitis inferior
longus atlantis

Mm. transversospinales occur in bundles, connecting each vertebra with the transverse processes or diapophyses, as the case may be, of the one next craniad. These really include the interspinales as well, but the fibers are extremely involved and difficult to segregate with precision.

This series is innervated by branches from the spinal nerves.

M. rectus capitis posterior major (figs. 11, 24) has origin from the lateral surface of the spine of the axis. Insertion is upon the supraoccipital from the rectus fossa laterad to the latero-caudal process of the occiput.

M. rectus capitis posterior minor (fig. 24) is situated medio-ventrad (deep) to the last. Origin is from the medial portion of the atlas, and insertion is upon the supraoccipital from the medial ridge laterad to the rectus fossa.

M. rectus capitis lateralis (figs. 8, 11, 24) has origin from the cranial part of the transverse process of the atlas, with insertion upon the slight extension of the angle of the occiput running ventrad from the process at its inferolateral end. In *Teonoma* this muscle seems to be not so well developed.

M. obliquus capitis superior (figs. 8, 10, 11, 24) has origin from the ventral border of the transverse process of the atlas, with insertion upon the exoccipital mediad to the mastoid and the caudal face of the paroccipital process.

M. obliquus capitis inferior (fig. 11). Origin is from the caudal half of the lateral surface of the spine of the axis, with insertion along most of the dorsal surface of the transverse process of the atlas.

M. longus atlantis (fig. 11) has origin from the transverse processes of the third, fourth and fifth cervical vertebrae, with insertion onto the caudal portion of the transverse process of the atlas. In *Teonoma* origin seems to be from the third and fourth vertebrae only.

All of these deep, intrinsic back muscles save the interspinales are innervated by the suboccipital nerve.

E. Muscles of the tail

Each half of the tail has two flexors, two extensors, and two abductors, these being

Mm. flexor caudae brevis   extensor caudae lateralis
    flexor caudae longus   abductor caudae externus
    extensor caudae medialis   abductor caudae internus

M. flexor caudae brevis (figs. 7, 12) has origin from the ventral surface of all the sacral and first four or five of the caudal vertebrae, close to the midventral line. The several tendons developing extend caudad with those of the flexor longus.

M. flexor caudae longus (figs. 7, 12). The more cranial portion of this powerful muscle lies deep (dorsad) to the psoas magnus. Origin is from the ventral surfaces of the centra and diapophyses of the vertebrae caudad from and including the fifth lumbar. Numerous tendons are developed which are inserted onto the caudal vertebrae.

Better terms to use for the flexors of the tail in the lower mammals would be anticus and posticus instead of brevis and longus, but the more usual nomenclature is retained for the present.

M. extensor caudae medialis (figs. 6, 12) is the muscle lying medio-dorsad upon the tail, it being a continuation of the multifidis spinae. Origin of its fibers is from the spinous processes of the sacral and a few of the caudal vertebrae. Tendons developing are inserted onto the dorsa of the vertebrae farther caudad.

In *Teonoma* this muscle is better developed than in either of the other subgenera.

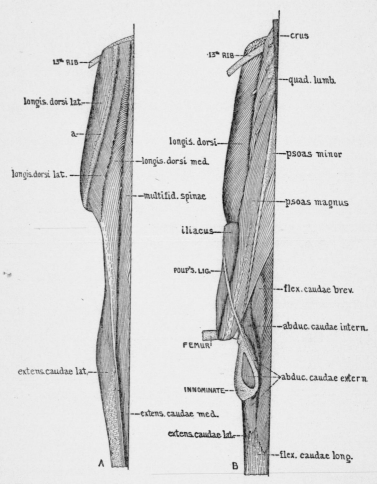

Fig. 12. Lumbar, sacral, and anterior caudal muscles of the vertebral region of *Homodontomys*. *A*, Supravertebral muscles (*a* representing deep lumbodorsal fascia, cut). *B*, Subvertebral muscles.

M. extensor caudae lateralis (figs. 6, 7, 12) is the caudal continuation of the longissimus dorsi medialis. Its fibers have deep origin from the diapophyses of the sacral and caudal vertebrae. The long, slender tendons which are developed from them pass to the dorsal part of the caudal vertebrae farther caudad.

M. abductor caudae externus (figs. 7, 12, 33) has origin from the medial border of the pubis extending from the symphysis to a point mediad of the acetabulum. It is separated from its fellow of the opposite side by the urethra and rectum. Insertion is upon the diapophyses of the first five caudal vertebrae.

M. abductor caudae internus (figs. 12, 33) has origin along the medio-ventral border of the ilium from the point of articulation with the sacrum caudad to the iliopectineal eminence. It passes caudad partly mediad to the abductor caudae externus, and tendons extending from it join those of the flexor caudae muscle.

The muscles of the tail are served by the coccygeal branches of the spinal nerves, not followed in the present instance.

F. Perineal musculature

Only four of these, exclusive of the sphincter ani internus layer (p. 97) occur with sufficient distinctness to merit recognition, and of these the external sphincter is the only one common to the two sexes. There probably are vestigeal fibers of other muscles, but if so their definition is too poor for their inclusion in the present work to be justified.

Mm. sphincter ani externus	bulbocavernosus
ischiocavernosus	compressor urethrae

M. sphincter ani externus (figs. 6, 21) occurs as a thin muscle band surrounding the anus, and to all intents it may be considered as an unpaired muscle. Insertion is upon the body of the urethra in the male, and the cervix uteri in the female.

M. ischiocavernosus (figs. 21, 32, 33) in the male takes origin for about 4 mm. from the caudal border of the ischium, with insertion upon the latero-distal portion of the body of the urethra. It invests a part of the corpus cavernosum.

M. bulbocavernosus (fig. 21). The homology of this with the muscle of the same name in the cat is uncertain because of the fact that what are herein termed the bulbs of the corpora cavernosa urethrae or corpora spongiosa, may be a separate organ with special function. At any rate, the fibers of this muscle, which are defined with some difficulty in animals which are sexually inactive, run obliquely laterad as they pass forward, investing the medial portion of each bulb.

M. compressor urethrae (fig. 21) is an unpaired muscle in the male, its fibers running in a circular course about the body of the urethra.

MUSCLES OF THE ANTERIOR LIMB

The muscles of the anterior limb fall naturally under the following headings:

> A. Muscles of the shoulder girdle
> B. Muscles of the upper arm
> C. Muscles of the forearm
> D. Muscles of the hand

A. MUSCLES OF THE SHOULDER GIRDLE

The muscles of the shoulder girdle number seven, as follows:

Mm. supraspinatus　　　　　　teres minor
　　infraspinatus　　　　　　teres major
　　clavo-acromiodeltoideus　　subscapularis
　　spinodeltoideus

M. supraspinatus (figs. 6, 13, 28, 29) occurs in two parts which are separable with fair ease. The more superficial one, whose ectal belly is invested with an aponeurosis, arises from the entire dorsal border of the spine of the scapula. Many of its fibers insert upon an aponeurosis which occurs deep between it and the other division, while the main insertion is onto the greater tuberosity of the humerus. The other, more cranial portion, arises from the supraspinous fossa of the scapula and is also inserted onto the greater tuberosity.

M. infraspinatus (figs. 6, 13, 28) has origin from the whole of the infraspinal surface of the scapula. About midway of the muscle an aponeurosis appears, and from this point it is bipennated. Insertion is by muscle fibers and by a tendon developed from its aponeurosis upon the greater tuberosity of the humerus.

M. clavo-acromiodeltoideus (figs. 6, 7, 13, 28, 29). In the present genus the clavo- and acromiodeltoids are considered as indivisible, the portions of the muscle corresponding to these two parts having their fibers converging to a tendinous division between them, so that the appearance is that of a single, bipennated muscle. The part corresponding to the clavodeltoid arises from the ventral border of the clavicle, with insertion upon the tendinous division between this and the acromiodeltoid, and upon the medial border of the deltoid ridge of the humerus. The part corresponding to the acromiodeltoid has origin from the cranio-ventral border of the acromion, while insertion is onto the tendinous division common to this and the preceding portion, and upon the lateral border of the deltoid ridge of the humerus. This part of the muscle directly overlies the insertional end of the spinodeltoid.

In *Teonoma* the origin of the acromiodeltoid is slightly more extensive.

M. spinodeltoideus (figs. 6, 28) arises from the caudal border of the entire spine of the scapula, although the dorsal 8 mm. is lightly aponeurotic and without muscle fibers. It passes beneath the acromiodeltoid and is inserted upon the deltoid ridge of the humerus.

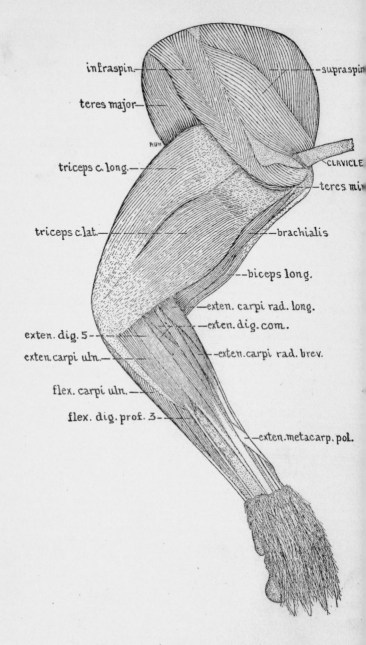

infraspin.

teres major

triceps c. long.

triceps c. lat.

exten. dig. 5

exten. carpi uln.

flex. carpi uln.

flex. dig. prof. 3

supraspin

CLAVICLE

teres mi

brachialis

biceps long.

exten. carpi rad. long.

exten. dig. com.

exten. carpi rad. brev.

exten. metacarp. pol.

Fig. 13. Superficial musculature of the right fore leg of *Teon*

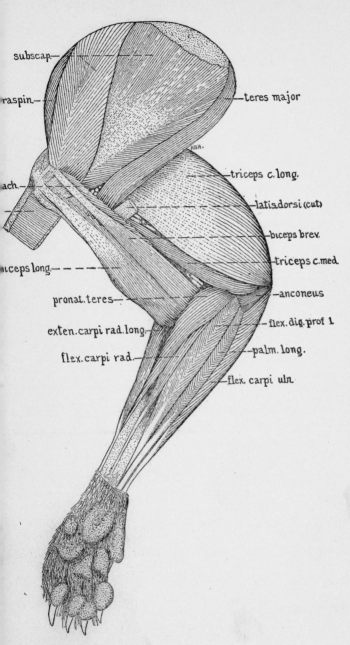

subscap.—

raspin—

—teres major

ach.—

—triceps c. long.

—latis.dorsi (cut)

—biceps brev.

—triceps c. med.

biceps long—

—anconeus

pronat. teres—

—flex. dig. prof 1

exten. carpi rad. long—

—palm. long.

flex. carpi rad.—

—flex. carpi uln.

Lateral aspect. B, Medial aspect (epitrochlearis removed)

M. teres minor (figs. 13, 28) is a small muscle whose fibers take origin from the lateral surface of an aponeurotic sheet extending along the axillary border of the scapula laterad to that of the caput longus of the triceps. Extending deep to the insertional portion of the infraspinatus, insertion is onto the greater tuberosity of the humerus. The muscle is not very well developed in the present subgenus and may easily be confused with a part of the infraspinatus, but in *Neotoma* and *Teonoma* it is more distinct.

M. teres major (figs. 6, 7, 13, 28, 29) is a thick muscle arising from the ventral portion of the glenovertebral angle of the scapula. Its origin is partly by muscle fibers and partly by aponeurosis upon its ental belly, from which latter some of the fibers of the subscapularis have origin. It passes over the fossa teres major of the scapula to its insertion by a tendon onto the process of the medial ridge of the humerus, adjoining and partially deep to the insertion of the latissimus dorsi.

M. subscapularis (figs. 7, 13, 29) occupies the medial surface of the scapula and is quite complex, being incompletely separable into several parts. In reality there would seem to be two main divisions, although individual variation in the exact grouping of the fibers is great and the two sides of a single specimen may be somewhat asymmetrical in this respect. The more cranial division is in part superficial to the other. It arises from the craniodorsal portion of the scapula, cranio-dorsad of the slight subscapular ridge. The more caudal division arises from the remainder of the medial face of the scapula. It develops a superficial aponeurosis onto which the more caudal fibers of the muscle are pennated. The common insertion is upon the caudal portion of the lesser tuberosity of the humerus just deep to the original end of the biceps.

The innervation of all these muscles of the shoulder girdle is by various branches of the fifth and sixth cervical nerves.

B. MUSCLES OF THE UPPER ARM

The muscles of the upper arm or brachium consist of flexors and extensors. Of flexors there are three, namely the

Mm. biceps brachii
coracobrachialis
brachialis

M. biceps brachii (figs. 6, 7, 13, 29) arises by two heads. The longer has origin by a tendon from the bicipital process upon the superior margin of the glenoid cavity and passes craniad over the bicipital groove between the two tuberosities of the humerus. It is barely separable in *Homodontomys* and *Neotoma*, but in *Teonoma* there are two rather distinct divisions, the smaller slip lying upon the deep belly, and being probably one-tenth the mass, of the larger.

The short head arises from the coracoid process by the tendon that is common to it and the coracobrachialis. It does not join the long head until at the insertion, common to both, which is by tendon onto the ulnar border of the radius near its head.

M. coracobrachialis (figs. 13, 29) is single in the present genus. Origin is by the tendon common to this and the short head of the biceps. It passes distad, mostly deep to the latter muscle and craniad of the triceps medialis, and is inserted along the medio-cranial border of the humerus for its distal two-fifths, including the medial epicondyloid ridge.

M. brachialis (figs. 6, 13, 28, 29) arises by two heads. The longer has origin from the lateral and caudal parts of the neck of the humerus and a part of the greater tuberosity, and passes distad along the lateral side of the deltoid ridge, to be joined by the shorter head arising from the cranial border of the shaft lying distad of the deltoid ridge. The tendinous termination of the muscle, common to both heads, then extends deep to the biceps and is inserted onto the brachial ridge of the medial border of the ulna.

These three flexor muscles are served by the musculo-cutaneous nerve.

Of *extensors* there are the following five:

Mm. epitrochlearis   triceps medialis
    triceps longus   anconeus
    triceps lateralis

M. epitrochlearis (figs. 7, 29) is the most superficial muscle of the inner brachium, and has origin by stout aponeurosis from the medio-distal portion of the latissimus dorsi. Insertion is upon the superficial fascia over the inner arm proximad and distad of the elbow.

In *Teonoma* it is slightly heavier.

The triceps brachii had better be treated as three distinct muscles, as follows:

M. triceps longus (figs. 6, 7, 13, 29) has origin by muscle fibers and aponeurosis upon its medial belly for some 10 mm. near the distal end of the axillary border of the scapula. Insertion is by a stout tendon onto the proximal end of the olecranon.

In *Teonoma* origin is slightly broader.

M. triceps lateralis (figs. 6, 13, 28) has origin by aponeurosis from the greater tuberosity of the humerus. Insertion is by aponeurosis for a distance of some 10 mm. along the proximal portion of the caudal border of the ulna.

M. triceps medialis (figs. 6, 13, 28, 29) arises along the posterior border of the shaft of the humerus beginning just distad of its medial process, and insertion is by muscle and tendon fibers onto the dorsal surface of the olecranon.

M. anconeus (figs. 13, 29) is a very short muscle located superficially upon the medial side of the elbow. It has origin from the medio-caudal part of the medial epicondyle of the humerus and passes to an insertion upon the extremity of the olecranon. Innervation of these five extensor muscles is by the radial nerve.

C. MUSCLES OF THE FOREARM

The muscles of the forearm or antibrachium may also be classed as flexors and extensors.

Of *flexors* there are seven, these being

Mm. palmaris longus   flexor carpi radialis
     pronator teres   pronator quadratus
     flexor digitorum sublimis   flexor carpi ulnaris
     flexor digitorum profundus

M. palmaris longus (figs. 13, 15, 29) is a bipennated muscle arising by tendon fibers from the medio-distal part of the medial epicondyle of the humerus. The broad tendon extending from it is inserted into the palmar fascia.

M. pronator teres (figs. 13, 29) has origin from the medial epicondyle and the aponeurosis common to this muscle and the flexor carpi radialis. Insertion is along the middle half of the medial border of the radius.

M. flexor digitorum sublimis (figs. 14, 15, 29) is simple and lies deep to the palmaris longus and the first head of the flexor digitorum profundus. It originates from the medial epicondyle of the humerus. Three tendons leave the muscle mass and passing superficial to most of the other palmar tendons, each branch extends to one of the three middle digits.

In *Teonoma* the muscle is larger and there are *four* divisions of the tendon, the fourth extending to digit five.

M. flexor digitorum profundus (figs. 13, 14, 15, 29) arises by three heads, as follows:

Caput 1 is a bipennated muscle, superficial to and lying medio-craniad of the palmaris longus. It has origin from the medial epicondyle of the humerus and deep attachment to the flexor carpi radialis. Its stout tendon passes deep to the branches of the flexor digitorum sublimis and diverges in two parts, passing respectively to digits two and three.

Caput 2 is a slender slip arising from the medial epicondyle of the humerus deep to the flexor digitorum sublimis. Its tendon is inserted into the common palmar tendon.

Caput 3 is single and may be considered as a fusion of the ulnar and radial heads that are distinct in many rodents.

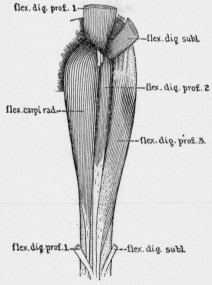

flex. dig. prof. 1--
--flex. dig. subl.
flex. dig. prof. 2
flex. carpi rad.--
--flex. dig. prof. 3.
flex. dig. prof. 1--
--flex. dig. subl.

Fig. 14. Deep flexors of the medial aspect of the right forearm of *Teonoma*.

It lies deep mostly to caput 2 and the flexor carpi radialis, and has a strong aponeurosis upon its superficial belly. It arises from the second to fourth fifths of the caudal border of the ulna, and from the proximal half of the radius. Its aponeurosis converges to a broad, thick tendon, heavier upon its lateral border, and this constitutes the main portion of the palmar tendon. This divides into five branches, four of them stout and passing to the lateral four digits, and the fifth, which is very slender, to the thumb.

M. flexor carpi radialis (figs. 13, 14, 15, 29) is located between the pronator teres and caput 1 of the flexor digitorum profundus, and has origin from the medial epicondyle deep to the origin of the latter muscle. Its slender tendon extends deep to the common tendon beneath tough, overlying tissue, and is inserted onto the base of metacarpus two only.

M. pronator quadratus (fig. 29) lies deep to the flexors and has origin from the distal half of the ulna. The fibers pass obliquely to their insertions upon the neighboring border of the radius.

M. flexor carpi ulnaris (figs. 13, 15, 29) which is single in the present genus and the largest muscle of the antebrachium, has origin chiefly from the medial portion of the olecranon and from the proximal two-fifths of the medio-caudal border of the ulna. There is also slight attachment to the medial epicondyle of the humerus. Its broad tendon is inserted upon the tuberosity of the pisiform bone.

The flexors of the forearm are all supplied by the median nerve. A branch of the ulnar nerve to the digitorum profundus may also occur but was not demonstrated.

Of *extensors* there are eight, consisting of

Mm. extensor digitorum communis   extensor carpi ulnaris
    extensor metacarpi pollicis   extensor carpi radialis longus
    extensor indicis   extensor carpi radialis brevis
    extensor digiti quinti   supinator

M. extensor digitorum communis (figs. 13, 15, 28). In *Homodontomys* this muscle is not divisible with certainty, although the tendons extending from it are with insertions as in *Teonoma*. In the latter subgenus this muscle mass is considerably more robust and upon its superficial surface is easily divisible into three parts, although there is interconnection of the deeper fibers between them. They all arise from the lateral epicondyle of the humerus proximad to the origin of the extensor digiti quinti. The tendons are stouter than in *Homodontomys* and as usual, all pass in a cluster beneath the transverse ligament. The more lateral head of this muscle develops a single tendon which splits in two, one branch passing to the medial dorsum of digit five and the other to the lateral dorsum of digit three. The head next mediad is the deepest of the three, with shortest belly. From the fibers extend two tendons which pass to the medial dorsum respectively of digits three and four. The most medial head develops a single tendon which extends to the medial dorsum of digit two. Due to the tenuousness of the distal ends of these tendons one can not be positive whether the insertion is upon the first or second phalanx.

M. extensor metacarpi pollicis (figs. 13, 15, 28) is a bipennated muscle arising deep to the extensor carpi ulnaris. It has origin from the proximal three-fifths of the radial surface of the ulna and half the ulnar surface of the radius. The broad tendon extending from it passes obliquely mediad from beneath the tendons of the extensor digitorum communis, over the tendons of the two extensores carpi radiales, and to its insertion upon the medial base of metacarpus one.

M. extensor indicis (figs. 15, 28). Origin of this very slender muscle is from the proximal half of the dorsocranial border of the lateral ridge of the ulna deep to the extensor carpi ulnaris. Its tendon passes over the carpal groove beneath the tendons of the extensor digitorum communis, and splitting in two, the more robust branch passes to the lateral dorsum of digit two, while a broader, though very thin and transparent, extension is inserted upon digit one.

M. extensor digiti quinti (figs. 13, 15, 28) lies dorso-

craniad of the last. Origin is from the lateral epicondyle
of the humerus distad of the origin of the extensor digitorum
communis. The tendon divides and with those of the
last-mentioned muscle, passes beneath the transverse ligament. The two divisions of the tendon then are inserted
upon the lateral side of the dorsum of digits four and five.

M. extensor carpi ulnaris (figs. 13, 15, 28) has origin
from the distal part of the lateral epicondyle of the humerus.
Passing along the dorso-cranial part of the shaft of the

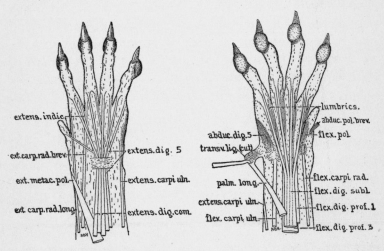

FIG. 15. Right manus of *Teonoma*, showing tendons and superficial musculature. *A*, Dorsal aspect. *B*, Palmar aspect.

ulna, insertion is by a tendon beneath the transverse
ligament and onto the lateral side of the base of metacarpus five.

M. extensor carpi radialis longus (figs. 13, 15, 28)
is the most proximal muscle having origin upon the lateral
epicondyloid ridge of the humerus. Its tendon passes
with that of the extensor carpi radialis brevis over the
carpus mediad to its center and is inserted upon the medial
dorsum of metacarpus two.

M. extensor carpi radialis brevis (figs. 13, 15, 28) has origin from the lateral epicondyloid ridge of the humerus between the origins of the extensores digitorum communis and carpi radialis longus. The latter muscle covers most of it. It develops a broad tendon which is inserted upon the medial dorsum of metacarpus three.

M. supinator (fig. 28) is the deepest muscle of the lateral antibrachium. It has origin by a stout tendon from the lateral side of the annular ligament of the radius. Insertion is upon the proximal half of the cranio-lateral part of the radius.

All of these extensor muscles of the forearm are innervated by the deep branch of the radial, or interosseus nerve.

D. MUSCLES OF THE HAND

There are undoubtedly vestiges of a number of muscles in the manus of this genus, but only four of them are sufficiently distinct for certain differentiation without special microscopical investigation. These are

Mm. lumbricales   abductor digiti quinti
       abductor pollicis brevis   flexor pollicis

Mm. lumbricales (fig. 15) apparently number four, and there are, of course, several interossei present, but they are so small and fragile that their definition is at best unsatisfactory, and they, together with rudiments of such muscles as the opponens, are not described.

M. abductor pollicis brevis (fig. 15) is a mere shred of muscle passing apparently from the base of the falciform to the thumb.

M. abductor digiti quinti (fig. 18) is a quite conspicuous muscle upon the lateral side of the palm. Origin is from the pisiform, with insertion upon the proximal phalanx of digit five.

M. flexor pollicis (fig. 15) arises from the scapholunar bone, with insertion apparently onto the proximal phalanx of the thumb.

The innervation of the smaller muscles of the hand was not sought.

MUSCLES OF THE POSTERIOR LIMB

As the muscles of the posterior limb are the most important to the present paper, and serious doubt was entertained regarding the homology of one of them, it was found advisable thoroughly to investigate the innervation of the hind leg. For the same reasons and because the lumbar plexus was found to differ to an important degree from that of the cat and man, it is here figured and will be discussed.

The nerves of the lumbar plexus pass caudad deep within the psoas major, as usual. The N. femoralis arises chiefly from the third lumbar nerve, but smaller branches come also from the second and fourth. It is normal in extending into the femoral or Scarpa's triangle and thence distad upon the medial surface of the thigh, sending a small branch to the pectineus. The N. obturatorius arises from the second and third nerves by means of a part of the femoralis, and also from the fourth, by a portion of the ischiaticus. It passes to the lateral side of the pelvis through the obturator foramen at its extreme cranial border. The N. ischiaticus arises from the fourth and fifth lumbar nerves only. It passes over the sciatic notch caudad to the level of the acetabulum as usual, but sends off a small branch, the N. gluteus superior, over the gluteal notch of the ilium just caudad of its postero-inferior spine. This penetrates the iliacus and deeper gluteal muscles. The N. pudendus arises from the sixth lumbar nerve and passes just mediad to the obturator internus to the vicinity of the superior tuberosity of the ischium.

The muscles of the posterior limb fall naturally under the following headings:

A. Muscles of the hip
B. Muscles of the thigh
C. Muscles of the leg
D. Muscles of the foot

A. MUSCLES OF THE HIP

The muscles segregated under this heading occur in three groups; namely,

1. Iliopsoas group
2. Gluteal group
3. Obturator group

1. Iliopsoas group

This is composed of the

Mm. psoas minor
psoas magnus
iliacus

M. psoas minor (figs. 12, 33) has fleshy origin from the centra apparently only of the second and third lumbar vertebrae. An aponeurotic tendon develops which passes superficially (ventrad) over the psoas magnus to its slender insertion upon the slight psoas process ventrad of the acetabulum. A very light, transparent but tough aponeurosis connects a portion of the medial border of this tendon with the centra of the last lumbar and first two sacral vertebrae. In *Neotoma* and *Teonoma* origin seems to be from the first lumbar vertebra as well.

M. psoas magnus (figs. 12, 33) has origin, deep to the psoas minor, from the centra of all (possibly not the first) of the lumbar vertebrae. The fibers are bipennated onto an aponeurotic tendon and this, with some of the muscle fibers, is inserted onto the cranial border of the lesser trochanter of the femur.

The innervation of the two psoas muscles is by branches of the lumbar nerves.

M. iliacus (figs. 6, 12, 17, 32, 33) is the deepest of the muscles of the ilium from the lateral aspect. It arises upon the inferior border of the crest of the ilium caudad along the iliacal ridge almost to the femoral process. It

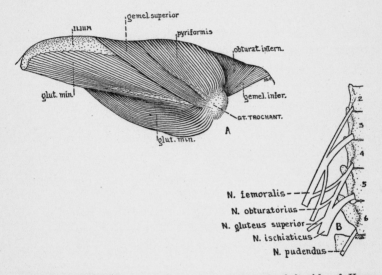

Fig. 16. *A*, Deeper gluteal musculature upon the left side of *Homodontomys*, with three most superficial glutei removed.

B, Semidiagrammatic presentation of right lumbar plexus of *Homodontomys*. (Last five lumbar and first sacral vertebrae shown on right.)

is inserted upon the cranial border of the lesser trochanter of the femur.

The innervation of the iliacus is by the femoral nerve.

2. Gluteal group

This group comprises the

Mm. gluteus superficialis   gluteus medius
    gluteus maximus   gluteus minimus

M. gluteus superficialis (figs. 6, 7, 32, 33). This is a muscle consisting of what are usually termed tensor fasciae latae or femoris, and sartorius. Because it is usually treated incorrectly it had better be called the gluteus superficialis. It has two origins and two insertions, and hence, although indivisible, it should be described in two parts.

Pars **anterior** arises from the cranial part of the ventral border of the ilium. Its latero-caudal portion is continuous with and inseparable from the posterior part, and insertion is weakly onto the fascia just proximad of the knee. In those lower mammals in which this muscle is present it seems invariably to have been called sartorius. In position and action it is somewhat analogous to that muscle, but were it homologous, the innervation would be by the femoral nerve. Such is not the case, however, for it is served by a branch of the N. gluteus superior, a fact established by the dissection of three specimens. It should be considered as a specialization of the posterior part of this muscle. In *Teonoma* this is somewhat heavier and extends farther caudad upon the medial side of the leg.

Pars **posterior** takes origin broadly from the dorsal fascia, and passing latero-ventrad, the fibers converge to an insertion by aponeurosis upon the lateral crest of the femur. This part is undoubtedly homologous with the tensor fasciae latae, but it is also a part of the gluteal mass, in action, location and innervation.

As already mentioned the innervation of this muscle is by the superior gluteal nerve.

M. gluteus maximus (figs. 6, 32). I do not agree with Parsons (1894, p. 282; 1896, p. 178) in considering that this muscle forms part of the tensor latae (or gluteus superficialis) sheet. I do not know what he had in mind, but the gluteus maximus is perfectly distinct in most rodents which I have dissected, occupying its normal position. When not distinct it should be considered as having fused with the gluteus medius. Origin from the deeper dorsal fascia extends from about the last lumbar to the third sacral vertebrae. This part of the muscle is very thin, and some of its deeper fibers are only with difficulty separable from the gluteus medius, which lies deep to most of the gluteus maximus. It passes just caudad of the head of the femur and is inserted for a distance of some 7 mm. upon the caudo-lateral border of the great trochanter and the lateral ridge adjoining.

In *Neotoma* and *Teonoma* the insertional portion is slightly broader.

The gluteus maximus is served by the inferior gluteal nerve.

M. gluteus medius (figs. 6, 32) has origin from the superior gluteal fossa of the ilium, particularly the cranial border, and from the dorsal fascia. Insertion is onto the proximo-medial part of the great trochanter.

M. gluteus minimus (figs. 6, 16, 32) is a rather complicated muscle, being partly bipennated and lying chiefly deep to the gluteus medius, its lateral edge only being visible before transecting the latter. Origin is from the lateral ridge of the ilium and its inferior gluteal fossa caudad, with origin of its ventral portion also from an aponeurotic sheet arising from the inferior border of the ilium. Insertion is by tendon fibers onto the great trochanter of the femur.

Innervation of the glutei medius and minimus is by the superior gluteal nerve.

3. Obturator group

The muscles of this group, numbering six, consist of

Mm. gemellus superior	gemellus inferior
pyriformis	quadratus femoris
obturator internus	obturator externus

M. gemellus superior (figs. 16, 32) arises along the caudal part of the dorsal border of the ilium caudad almost to the acetabulum. Insertion is onto the medial portion of the great trochanter of the femur.

In *Teonoma* the muscle is broader but is separable from the gluteus medius only with some difficulty.

M. pyriformis (figs. 16, 32, 33) is a short muscle lying immediately deep to a part of the gluteus medius and directly over the sciatic nerve. Origin is from the diapophyses of the first two (?) sacral vertebrae, and insertion is onto the great trochanter of the femur. Contrary to the statement of Parsons (1894, p. 283) the closest relationship of this muscle is with the gluteus medius, and not the gluteus minimus. This is so in the case of the gemellus superior, however, and from his statements as to origins, it seems that he may have confused this with the pyriformis, overlooking the true pyriformis entirely.

In *Teonoma* this seems not to be separable from the gluteus medius with any surety.

M. obturator internus (figs. 16, 17, 33) has origin from the medial surface of the ischium caudad and craniad of the obturator foramen. It converges and passes over the dorsal border of the ischium between its tuber superior and the acetabulum, and is inserted into the trochanteric fossa. The insertional part of this muscle forms a portion of the floor of the intramuscular passage for the sciatic nerve.

M. gemellus inferior (figs. 16, 17, 32). It is only by its origin that this muscle may be readily distinguished. It arises from the gemellus fossa upon the ischium just craniad of the superior tuberosity, and is inseparably inserted onto the caudal margin of the obturator internus near its insertion.

M. quadratus femoris (figs. 17, 32, 33) has origin from the lateral surface of the ischium ventrad and craniad of its superior tuberosity. It converges sharply to its insertion upon the caudal base of the lesser trochanter. It is thus intermediate in position between the obturators externus and internus.

The innervation of these five muscles is by branches from the sacral plexus.

M. obturator externus (figs. 32, 33) has origin from the entire lateral border of the obturator foramen except its extreme cranial portion. Converging, it passes just ventrad of the obturator internus to an insertion deep to the latter and into the trochanteric fossa.

Innervation of this muscle is by the N. obturatorius.

B. MUSCLES OF THE THIGH

The muscles of the thigh consist of flexors, extensors and adductors.

The *flexors* number six as follows:

Mm. semimembranosus anticus
    semimembranosus posticus
    semitendinosus

biceps femoris anticus
biceps femoris posticus
tenuissimus

The semimembranosus is double, as is so often the case, and one of the slips is probably the most variable muscle in the body.

M. semimembranosus anticus (figs. 6, 32, 33) is exceedingly variable in its origin. In a selected specimen it arose by two heads. The larger and more superficial of these extended from the fascia investing the sacrocaudal muscles, while the deeper head, but two millimeters in width, arose by tendon fibers from the ischium just craniad of its superior tuberosity. The two heads united immediately and the slender muscle resulting passed upon the medial side of the leg, deep to the medial part of the insertion of the adductor femoris, to an insertion upon the tibia just distad of the medial tuberosity. In the four specimens of *Homodontomys* in which this point was investigated this muscle arose by two heads from the ischium and fascia in a single specimen, by a single head from the fascia in one instance, and a single head from the ischium in the other two.

In *Neotoma*, origin was by two heads, the one from the ischium being much the smaller, in one specimen, and by a single head from the fascia in two cases. In three specimens of *Teonoma* origin was by one head from the ischium only. In this subgenus the insertional end is located a trifle farther craniad, so that by its position the insertional portion of the adductor femoris is completely separated into two slips.

M. semimembranosus posticus (figs. 6, 7, 32, 33) is much the more robust of the two, and arises from the superior tuberosity of the ischium and the adjoining caudal border of that bone. It passes to the medial side of the lower leg and is inserted by aponeurosis onto the tibial collateral ligament and the medial tuberosity of the tibia.

In *Teonoma* it is more robust and composed of coarser fibers, being readily divisible into numerous layers.

M. semitendinosus (figs. 6, 7, 32, 33) arises by two heads, the more dorsal or lateral one of which has origin from the fascia overlying the first two caudal vertebrae, rather than from the vertebrae proper. The much smaller ventral head arises from the tuberosity of the ischium partly superficial to the origin of the biceps posticus. The two heads shortly unite, the resulting muscle passing to the medial side of the calf to an insertion upon the superficial fascia.

The biceps femoris occurs in two divisions, distinct throughout their length.

M. biceps femoris anticus (figs. 6, 32) arises from the diapophyses apparently of the first two caudal vertebrae just deep to the origin of the semitendinosus, and extends to a narrow insertion upon the lateral border of the patella.

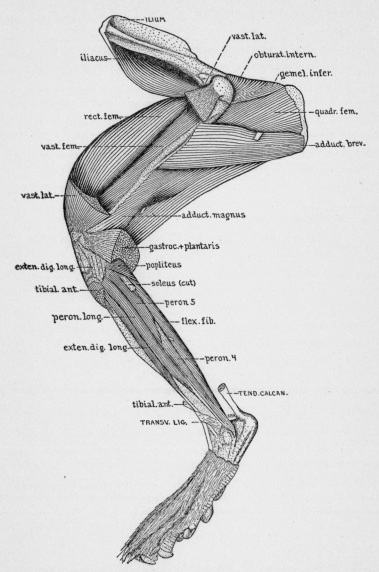

FIG. 17. Deeper muscles upon the lateral aspect of the left hind limb of *Teonoma*.

M. biceps femoris posticus (figs. 6, 32) has origin from the superior tuberosity of the ischium partly deep to the heads of the semitendinosus. Rapidly expanding it extends to an insertion upon the fascia of about half the cranial border of the lower leg.

M. tenuissimus (figs. 6, 32) is an exceedingly slender and fragile muscle which is easily overlooked. Origin is from the deeper dorsal fascia between the origins of the gluteus superficialis and biceps anticus. It passes deep to the biceps posticus and gluteus maximus, and extending distad, is inserted onto the fascia of the lateral side of the calf.

All of these six flexor muscles of the thigh are served by the N. ischiaticus.

The *extensors* of the thigh, numbering four and comprising the quadriceps femoris, are the

Mm. rectus femoris	vastus femoris
vastus lateralis	vastus medialis

M. rectus femoris (figs. 7, 17, 32, 33) is a strong muscle situated between the vastus lateralis and the other two vasti. Arising by a single head it is pennated proximad, and has origin by tendon fibers from the femoral process upon the ilium immediately craniad of the acetabulum. Investing aponeuroses develop upon its lateral and medial bellies, and these converge to a strong insertion upon the proximal border of the patella.

M. vastus lateralis (figs. 6, 7, 17, 32) has origin by tendon fibers from the disto-cranio-lateral part of the great trochanter. It extends in a thick mass superficial to the rectus femoris and vastus intermedius, curving slightly toward the medial surface of the leg to an insertion by tendon fibers onto the patella and patellar ligament.

M. vastus femoris (or intermedius) (figs. 17, 32, 33) has origin from practically the whole of the cranial border of the shaft of the femur in a pennated manner. The caudo-lateral fibers of the proximal portion show a tendency to be integral with the vastus lateralis. Insertion is onto the proximo-cranial portion of the capsule of the knee.

M. vastus medialis (figs. 7, 33) is located medio-caudad of the rectus femoris and has origin over a small area on the medial femur distad of the head. The fibers of the proximo-lateral portion are with some difficulty separable from the vastus femoris. Insertion is onto the capsule of the knee.

The innervation of the four extensors of the thigh is by the N. femoralis.

The *adductors* of the thigh are five, as follows:

Mm. pectineus   adductor brevis
gracilis   adductor magnus
adductor longus

M. pectineus (figs. 7, 32, 33) lies partly superficial upon the medial aspect of the leg between the adductor longus and the iliopectineal fossa or Scarpa's triangle. It has origin from the pectineal process ventrad of the acetabulum. Insertion is mostly fleshy upon the caudal border of the femur extending from the base of the lesser trochanter for almost half the length of the shaft.

The pectineus is the only muscle of the flexor group served by a branch of the N. femoralis.

M. gracilis (figs. 7, 32, 33) arises by two heads. The posterior one has fleshy origin from the caudal border of the ischium, while the anterior arises from the border of the pubis deep to the origin of the adductor longus. The contiguous borders of the two heads fuse and the insertion of the single muscle sheet thus formed is fascial upon the proximo-cranial border of the tibia.

In *Teonoma* both heads are broader and the origin of the cranial one is to all intents entirely hidden by the adductor longus. In these respects *Neotoma* is fairly intermediate between the other two subgenera.

The adductor mass of the thigh is divisible into three muscles. It is unfortunate that their established names are so misleading in the case of rodents; and yet it seems unwise to adopt others as substitutes just now.

M. adductor longus (figs. 7, 32, 33) is the shortest one of the adductors and is the more caudal one of the two, small, triangular muscles upon the medial surface of the leg. Its fleshy origin, partly superficial to that of the gracilis anticus, is from the pubis, extending from the midsymphysis forward to the pectineal process. It converges to a slender tendon which is inserted upon the caudal border midway of the femur and just distad of the pectineal insertion.

In *Teonoma* this muscle usually lies entirely superficial to the origin of the gracilis anticus, but there is some variation in this respect.

M. adductor brevis (figs. 6, 7, 17, 32, 33) is the more lateral and shorter one of the two remaining adductors. Its fleshy origin is along practically the entire length of the pubis between the adductor magnus and the obturator externus. Insertion is for a distance of about 12 mm. along the cranial border of the lateral crest of the femur, extending almost equidistantly either way from its most prominent point.

M. adductor magnus (figs. 6, 7, 17, 32, 33) has origin from the cranial two-thirds of the ventral pubis. Insertion begins immediately distad of the insertion of the adductor brevis along the remainder of the caudo-lateral border of the shaft of the femur. A portion curves around to infold the insertional end of the semimembranosus anticus, and passes to an insertion upon the medial portion of the capsule of the knee joint. The femoral artery, in passing from the iliopectineal fossa to the popliteal space, pierces the caudal border of the adductor magnus, as it does in man, and then extends between the more lateral portion of the insertional end of the latter muscle and the semimembranosus anticus.

In *Teonoma* the insertion of the last-mentioned muscle is located slightly more cranio-dorsad, so that the part of the adductor passing to the femoral epicondyle is completely separated from the remainder of the muscle, and the femoral artery thus passes between the two slips. This is also the case in *Neotoma*, but to a slightly lesser degree. Attention may be called to the fact that the adductor magnus is a double muscle, and its form and function among the lower Mammalia offers an interesting and important subject for study.

The innervation of the gracilis, adductores longus, brevis, and the more lateral part of the magnus, is by the obturator nerve, while the more medial portion of the last muscle is served by the N. ischiaticus.

C. MUSCLES OF THE LEG

The present scheme of muscle arrangement for the lower leg into groups containing flexors, extensors, and peroneal muscles, and based also on the innervation, seemingly shows a number of anomalies, for the flexor group as here presented contains muscles that both extend and flex the ankle. These muscles, nevertheless, comprise a flexor group and are similarly innervated, and this arrangement will be employed for the present.

The *flexor group*, then, of the lower leg contains the following eight muscles:

Mm. gastrocnemius medialis	popliteus
gastrocnemius lateralis	flexor digitorum longus
plantaris	flexor digitorum fibularis
soleus	tibialis posticus

The first four of these muscles compose the M. quadriceps surae, whose tendons extend to form the tendo calcaneus.

This group is unusually strong in the present genus, as it is in many rodents.

M. gastrocnemius medialis (figs. 7, 17, 33) has origin by muscle fibers and narrower superficial aponeurosis from the medial sesamoid bone and the adjoining portion of the femur. A sheet of aponeurosis extending distad from its ental belly is twisted, and passes to the tendo calcaneus upon its *lateral* border. The tibial nerve enters the calf between this muscle and the plantaris.

M. gastrocnemius lateralis (figs. 6, 17, 33) is more complicated. Superficially it is with difficulty separable into three portions—a disto-medial one, situated disto-laterad of the visible part of the plantaris; a proximo-medial one; and a lateral, lying superficial to the last and having origin by aponeurosis. Entad these three parts are curiously involved, the fibers joining a much crumpled sheet of aponeurosis. The common origin is from the lateral sesamoid and adjoining portion of the femur, and insertion is onto the tendo calcaneus.

In *Neotoma* and *Teonoma* the ental aponeurosis of the entire muscle is somewhat simpler and less folded, which probably means a weaker muscle.

M. plantaris (figs. 6, 7, 17, 32). The origin of this muscle, situated upon the caudal border of the calf and visible between the two gastrocnemii, is from the caudal portion of the lateral epicondyle of the femur and the tendinous tissue about the lateral sesamoid bone medio-proximad to that of the gastrocnemius lateralis. Its deep fibers are much involved with the ental aponeurosis of the last-mentioned muscle, and indeed, in *Homodontomys*, it is no more distinct, entally, than are the two medial portions of its lateral neighbor. It may readily be identified, however, by the fact that its tendon extends beyond the tendo calcaneus, passing over the heel to the sole. It there divides into two layers, although, in fact, the more superficial of these (the superficial plantar tendon) might with equal propriety be said to have its relationship rather with the flexor digitorum longus. Each of these layers sends four branches to the four lateral digits.

In one specimen of *Teonoma* the superficial plantar tendon sent a branch to each of the five digits.

M. soleus (figs. 6, 17, 32) is the deepest one of the Achillean muscles. It arises by a tendon from the caudal part of the head of the fibula, and its distal tendon joins the cranial border of the tendo calcaneus.

In one specimen of *Teonoma* there was a thread-like tendon arising from the medial shaft of the fibula, to which a few fibers of the central portion of the ental belly of the soleus were attached.

M. popliteus (figs. 7, 17, 32, 33) has a very small, tendinous origin from the lightly defined popliteal fossa upon the disto-caudal portion of the lateral epicondyle of the femur. Diverging and passing obliquely mediad, its insertion is along the proximal third of the me ial shaft of the tibia.

The following three muscles constitute the deep flexors of the calf.

M. flexor digitorum longus (figs. 7, 33) has fleshy origin along the second and third fifths of the medial ridge of the tibia, partly deep to the popliteus. Its fibers are bipennated onto its tendon, which passes along a groove upon the internal malleolus of the ankle, divides, sending one branch to the medial side of digit one, and a broader one to join the superficial tendon of the flexor fibularis.

M. flexor digitorum fibularis (flexor hallucis longus) (figs. 7, 17, 18, 33) is a large muscle occupying most of the space posteriorly between the tibia and fibula. Origin is from the medio-caudal head of the fibula and the adjacent portion of the tibial head, and from the medial border of the fibula for two-thirds its length. Its tendon passes mediad, between the astragalus and ankle to the sole, where it thickens before dividing, usually into five branches, one of which extends to the terminal phalanx of each digit. In a minority of the specimens examined of all three subgenera there were but four branches extending respectively to the four lateral digits.

M. tibialis posticus (figs. 7, 32, 33) has origin from the proximal portion of the lateral border of the medial ridge, chiefly deep to the flexor longus. The fibers are pennated onto its tendon, which passes over the medial ankle and is inserted onto the sesamoid bone of the tarsus.

The innervation of these eight flexors of the calf is by means of the tibial nerve.

The *extensor group* of the lower leg includes but three muscles, as follows:

> Mm. tibialis anticus
> extensor hallucis
> extensor digitorum longus

M. tibialis anticus (figs. 6, 7, 17, 18, 32, 33) originates from the cranio-lateral border of the head of the tibia; by aponeurotic fibers from the fibular collateral ligament of the knee; and from the fascia covering the proximal portion of the tibial shaft. The fibers of the latter portion are pennated upon the ental surface of the broad tendon which develops within the muscle. The distal tendon passes beneath the transverse ligament of the instep to the medial border of the pes and is inserted upon the entocuneiform bone.

M. extensor hallucis (figs. 6, 18, 32) is a very slender muscle lying between the tibialis anticus and extensor digitorum longus. It arises from the interosseous fascia between the tibia and fibula rather than from the border of the latter bone. Its feeble tendon passes beneath the transverse and crural ligaments in close relation with the tibialis anticus, and is inserted upon the dorsal aspect of the hallux.

M. extensor digitorum longus (figs. 6, 17, 18, 32) in reality constitutes an extensor digitorum communis, but the more usual name will be employed. It has origin by a long, flat tendon from the lateral epicondyle of the femur. It passes deep beneath the origin of the tibialis anticus and the rather slender muscular portion lies deep and caudad to the latter. Well proximad upon its belly an aponeurosis develops, which narrows to a tendon passing beneath the transverse ligament and over the instep. At about the transverse ligament it splits into four parts which shortly separate, each passing to the medio-cranial margin of one of the four lateral digits.

The three extensor muscles of the calf are served by the N. peroneus profundus.

The *peroneal group* of muscles, numbering four, is also very well developed in this genus. The interconnection between their fibers is very close, but one will have no trouble in dissecting them if he follows up their tendons. They consist of

Mm. peroneus longus   peroneus digiti quarti
       peroneus brevis   peroneus digiti quinti

M. peroneus longus (figs. 6, 17, 32, 33) has origin from the latero-cranial or peroneal process upon the head of the fibula. It passes superficially between the tibialis anticus and the peronei quarti and quinti. The superficial peroneal nerve passes deep between this and the last two muscles. Its tendon extends over the external malleolus and the peroneal groove on the medio-ventral part of the cuboid, and is inserted upon the ventral aspect of the ectocuneiform only (apparently not onto the first metatarsus, as Parsons (1894, p. 290) claims is the case in most rodents).

M. peroneus brevis (figs. 18, 32, 33) has origin along the entire medio-caudal shaft of the fibula and the portion of its head adjoining. Its tendon, which is the stoutest of all the peronei, passes over the external malleolus and is inserted upon the peroneal process at the base of metatarsus five.

M. peroneus digiti quarti (figs. 6, 17, 18, 32) usually has origin (as in fig. 17) from a tenuous aponeurosis investing the lateral belly of the peroneus quinti. Occasionally, however, the muscle extends farther proximad and has origin from the head of the fibula superficial to the peroneus quinti. Its tendon passes over the external malleolus and is inserted upon the lateral border of digit four. It is not until its tendon is followed proximad that this muscle is distinguishable from the peroneus digiti quinti.

In *Teonoma* the tendon divides into two, a branch extending to either side of digit four.

M. peroneus digiti quinti (figs. 17, 18, 32) has tenuous origin from the proximal portion of the latero-caudal head of the fibula. Its tendon, passing over the external malleolus with those of the other peronei, is inserted onto the lateral border of digit five.

The peroneal muscles are innervated by the N. peroneus superficialis.

D. MUSCLES OF THE FOOT

The interrelationship of some of the smaller muscles of the sole of the foot is so exceedingly close, and they are so tenuous, that it is not always possible without painstaking microscopical investigation to be absolutely certain in regard to their definition. The exposition of the muscles as here presented has been decided upon only after the dissection of a number of specimens, and the homology of all of them is not certain.

The muscles of the hind foot that were dissected with satisfactory certainty number eleven, as follows:

Mm. extensor digitorum brevis   abductor digiti quinti
    flexor digitorum brevis   flexor digiti quinti brevis

quadratus plantae   adductor digiti quarti
lumbricales   adductor digiti secundi
flexor hallucis   interossei
abductor hallucis

M. extensor digitorum brevis (fig. 18) is the only
muscle upon the dorsum of the pes. Origin of its few
fibers is from the cranial part of the calcaneal annular
ligament. Two thread-like tendons develop which extend
to insertions upon the extreme lateral sides of digits two
and three.

M. flexor digitorum brevis (fig. 18) constitutes the
main continuation, over the heel, of the plantaris. It develops muscle fibers upon both the ectal and ental surfaces of the deeper division of the plantar ligament of the
plantaris, which are inserted chiefly upon the lateral three
or four tendinous branches which pass, respectively, to the
four lateral digits. The lateral portion of the main tendon
consists of a separate tendinous slip, arising from the
membranous investment of the calcaneum.

M. quadratus plantae (accessorius) (fig. 18). This
muscle does not have two separate heads in the present
genus, although the origin is continuous both from the
ventral head of the os calcis, and fleshy from the lateral
and medial parts of this bone. Insertion is upon the
peroneal process of metatarsus five.

Mm. lumbricales (fig. 18) are four in number. They
develop from the tendon of the flexor fibularis, which
tendon is more intimately concerned with the latter muscle
than the digitorum longus, as is often the case. Their
insertions are upon the tendinous branches extending to
the four lateral digits.

M. flexor hallucis (fig. 18) seems to occur in two divisions. The first has origin from the entocuneiform and is
inserted onto the external tarso-phalangeal sesamoid. The
more medial division, which may really constitute one of

the interossei, has origin apparently from the ectocuneiform and is inserted onto the internal sesamoid of the same toe.

M. abductor hallucis (fig. 18) arises from the scaphoid and is inserted upon the border of the medial tarso-phalangeal sesamoid of the hallux.

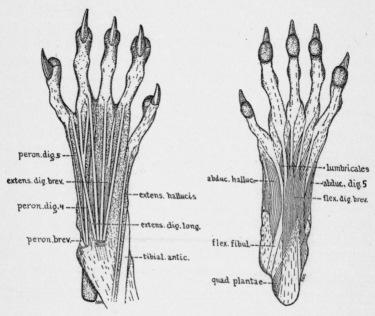

FIG. 18. *A*, Dorsal aspect of left pes of *Teonoma*, showing superficial tendons and muscle.

B, Plantar aspect of left pes of *Homodontomys*, showing superficial muscles and tendons.

M. abductor digiti quinti (fig. 18) has origin that is chiefly tendinous from the anterior portion of the calcaneum. Insertion is upon the lateral side of the first phalanx of digit five.

M. flexor digiti quinti brevis lies mediad to the abductor of this toe and must be carefully distinguished.

Its tendinous origin is also from the plantar process of the calcaneum, and insertion is upon the base of the first phalanx of digit five.

M. adductor digiti quarti has origin apparently from the entocuneiform and insertion upon the medial sesamoid of digit four.

M. adductor digiti secundi lies partly deep to the last, with origin from the ectocuneiform, and insertion onto the lateral sesamoid of digit two.

Mm. interossei are quite well developed and apparently number eight—two to each of the three middle digits and one internal to each of digits one and five. Origin is from the bases of the metatarsi, and insertion is upon the sesamoids of their respective digits.

CHAPTER VI

ALIMENTARY TRACT AND ADJACENT GLANDS

Mouth. Just caudad of the incisors there is upon either side a cartilaginous thickening of the cheek, constituting the oral sphincter pad. These are in no degree muscular, but they project from the ental surface of the cheek sufficiently and are so situated that the two effect complete closure of the mouth when the buccinator muscles are in normal tone, thus excluding undesirable particles of matter from the mouth. The more ventral portion of these pads is sparsely covered with short hairs, corresponding to the covering upon the integument of the lips, while the dorsal portion is invested with mucous membrane.

Beginning at the middle of the maxillary diastema and extending upon the inner cheek for about three millimeters caudad is a roughly circular, oral, bristle area upon either side. This, in *Homodontomys*, is not raised into an eminence and it is covered with a large number of fine bristles two or three millimeters long. These incline towards the gullet. A narrow band covered with fine hairs also extends from this along a fold in the cheek to the corner of the lips. In *Neotoma* this bristle area is slightly raised, and in *Teonoma*, still more so, constituting a marked, hairy pad.

The significance of this bristle area is obscure. It may be a remnant of former and greater specialization of the part, or may constitute the earlier stage of some adaptational organ. It is of some use, however, in that the backward-pointing bristles upon either side form a hairy barrier completely across the oral cavity at this point, allowing the free entrance of particles of food but hindering their egress.

The ridging of the mucous membrane upon the roof of

90

the mouth may be divided into two areas and classes, as follows:

The diastemal ridging occurs in the space between the incisors and the molariform teeth. In *Homodontomys* there is a narrow ridge parallel with the long axis of the skull extending from just caudad of the incisors. Posteriorly it enlarges to terminate in an eminence marked by a

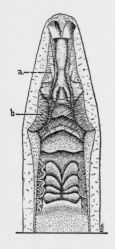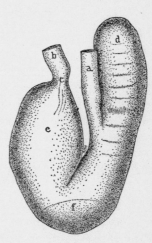

Fig. 19. *A*, Roof of the mouth of *Teonoma* with lower jaw removed, showing ridging, (*a*) sphincter pads, and (*b*) oral bristle areas.

B, Stomach of *Teonoma*, showing (*a*) oesophagus, (*b*) duodenum, (*c*) pyloric valve, (*d*) cardiac horn, (*e*) pyloric horn, (*f*) position of fundus gland.

slight, transverse crest. In sequence caudad to this there is a narrow, transverse ridge and two broader ones, the former of these two being obtusely angular. In *Neotoma* the caudal termination of the first ridge is larger, and in *Teonoma*, larger still, being in reality three parallel ridges joined at their bases. This variation in ridging is in response to slight differences in the shape of the oral sphincter pads of the respective subgenera, for the pads, through medial pressure, have molded the anterior ridging of the roof of the mouth.

The palatal ridging, situated upon the roof of the mouth between the rows of the molariform teeth, consists of two series of four transverse ridges, one series upon either side, separated by a medial sulcus. The two pairs most craniad slope partially medio-caudad. Posterior to these is a slightly-defined transverse prominence running uninterruptedly from one tooth row to the other.

The tongue is fleshy, of moderate size, and is not appreciably papilliferous.

Parotid gland (fig. 5). Each of these occurs in two, illy-defined divisions. The anterior one fills the angle of the jaw, lying well forward over a part of the masseter with one extension thrust dorsad in front of the base of the ear, and another behind it. Cranio-ventrad the two parotids almost meet. In this region they partly overlie the submaxillary glands. A parotid duct leaves either gland upon its medial surface several mm. (6–8) caudad of its cranial border and pierces the buccinator well towards the front of the mouth. The anterior margin of the posterior division lies superficial to the caudal border of the anterior one.

In *Teonoma* the gland, especially the posterior division, is somewhat smaller and decidedly thinner, with smaller lobulations. It is darker in color than in *Homodontomys*.

Submaxillary gland (fig. 5). The two glands lie in contact with each other along the median line of the throat. They are partly deep to the parotids (anterior divisions) and extend caudad well towards the chest.

In *Teonoma* they are a trifle shorter, extending not so far caudad, but broader, better defined, and probably more efficient than in *Homodontomys* or *Neotoma*. In the latter subgenus the parotids and submaxillaries are of the same color. In *Teonoma* the former are the darker.

The parotid glands secrete a liquid that is comparatively non-viscid, without mucin, and rich in ptyalin, which latter is especially active in the digestion of starchy foods. These glands are a trifle better developed in *Homodontomys* and *Neotoma* than in *Teonoma*, which fact conforms to expectations, for the food of the last subgenus is indicated as being the least starchy in character.

On the other hand, the secretion of the submaxillary glands is comparatively more viscid because containing more mucin, which acts as a lubricant during the deglutition of coarse, dry fodder, such as *Teonoma* uses in larger amount. In this subgenus the submaxillary glands are broader, better defined, and probably more efficient than in the other two, as previously mentioned.

Oesophagus. The more cephalic portion of this lies dorsad of the trachaea, but as it passes caudad it extends slightly laterad of the latter. In *Teonoma* it does not extend so far laterad. It is attached to the trachaea and the vertebrae by tissue. The length, from the larynx to the stomach, is from 60 to 75 mm., depending upon the size of the animal.

Stomach. This is U-shaped, the cardiac and pyloric divisions being very distinct, and the adjoining surfaces are connected to one another by tissue, thus bringing the oesophagus and duodenum into juxtaposition. When moderately distended with food, the stomach in two specimens measured 37 by 30 and 40 by 32, with thickness of 14 and 16 mm., respectively. Measuring from the base of the incisura angularis between the horns, the cardiac extended 24 and 22 mm., and the pyloric horn, 19 and 20 mm. The former was slightly muscular, with glandular folds upon its inner wall, but the pyloric horn was almost devoid of muscle fibers. At the base of the stomach upon its ental surface there was a sharply defined circular area, 20 mm. in diameter and about 2 mm. in thickness, of a reddish brown color in the preserved specimen, surrounded by stratified squamous epithelium. Bensley (1902) designates this area as a fundus gland. No histological examination of the present genus was made, but sections of the stomachs of allied, cricetine rodents show that the glands are tubular and of the parietal type. It is entirely possible that their high specialization and sharp differentiation is connected with some special function.

In *Neotoma* the stomach is more nearly spherical, measuring 32 by 33 by 14 in one specimen, and 29 by 39 by 15 mm. in another, and in muscularity is fairly intermediate between *Homodontomys* and *Neotoma*. The cardiac horn had a length of 20 mm. in one specimen and 22 in the other, while the pyloric horn measured 18 and 21 mm. respectively. In this subgenus the fundus gland was similar and 21 mm. in diameter.

In *Teonoma* the specialization is more pronounced, with longer horns to the stomach. In two specimens the latter member measured 41 by 27, and 48 by 27. The cardiac was heavily striated with tough muscle and glandular folds, and the pyloric horn was also well muscled. In places this portion of the stomach wall is 4 mm. thick, as compared to paper thin to one millimeter in *Homodontomys*. There is a definite constriction at the pyloric valve and the oesophagus joins the stomach at a point farther from the tip of the horn. In this subgenus the fundus area had a diameter of about 27 mm., was thicker, and of a dark green color, the last point probably being due to the herbaceous nature of the food.

Spleen. The spleen is located dorso-caudad upon the cardiac horn of the stomach. In a single specimen of *Teonoma* one-third of the spleen was bent at right angles to the remainder, but in all other examples it was straight. In *Homodontomys* it measured about 25 by 7 mm.; in *Neotoma* 28 by 7 mm.; and in *Teonoma*, 37 by 8 mm.

Pancreas. This is of considerable extent but is not unusual.

Small intestine. In most mammals the small intestine

is divisible into two tracts—the duodenum and Meckel's tract (see Mitchell, 1905)—not into three as in man. In this genus the two tracts are not differentiated save by means of the mesentery. Without undue extension the length of the small intestine, between the stomach and caecum, was 655 mm. in one specimen and 725 in another. The collapsed width of the duodenal portion was about 7 mm.

In three specimens of *Neotoma* the length of the small intestine was 480, 520, and 490 mm. In *Teonoma* it was much more capacious. The duodenal width was 12 to 13 mm., although farther caudad it was not quite so broad; and its length in two specimens was 815 and 825 mm.

Liver. The medial lobe of the liver is the largest. It is divisible into a right (the larger) and a left lobelet, between which is situated the gall bladder. In *Homodontomys* the medial border of the left lobelet lay superficial to that of the right in two specimens, while in two each of *Neotoma* and *Teonoma* the opposite condition obtained. The left lateral lobe is relatively smaller in *Homodontomys* and *Neotoma* than in *Teonoma*, but in the last it is almost if not quite as large as the medial lobe. The right lateral lobe is smaller still, and is divisible into a cranial (the larger) and a caudal lobelet. The flat, caudal lobe lies dorsad of the left lateral and is usually double, but was observed to be single in one individual of *Homodontomys*. In two specimens of each subgenus the cubic capacity of the liver was found to be constantly about 5 cc. in *Homodontomys*; 6.5 cc. in *Neotoma;* and 12 cc. in *Teonoma*. The precise functions of the liver are too involved and as yet too poorly understood for any interpretation of the significance of the much larger size of this organ in *Teonoma*. Suffice it to say that it probably reflects some detail regarding the normal diet.

Large intestine. The most interesting part of this is the

caecum, which is greatly developed in the present genus. In two specimens its length beyond the small intestine was 103 and 110 mm. The enlarged base was prolonged into the neck, of only slightly reduced diameter, between the caecum proper and the colic loops, which latter make two and one-quarter turns. In one specimen there was an additional reverse turn.

In three specimens of *Neotoma* the caecum was 85, 108, and 110 mm. in length, and as much as 27 mm. in diameter. The neck, posterior to the small intestine, was extremely well developed, of as large diameter as the caecum proper, and

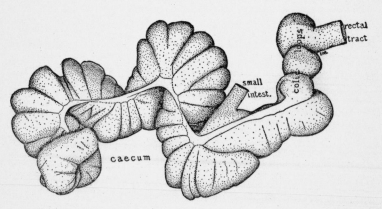

FIG. 20. Caecal portion of the large intestine of *Homodontomys*.

became only slightly smaller throughout its length of 25 mm. to the colic loops, which resembled those of *Teonoma*.

In *Teonoma* the caecum measured 120 and 118 mm. in two specimens. The neck was constricted and well differentiated from the caecum proper, being but 10 mm. in width, and 22 and 30 mm. in length, with thicker walls. In this subgenus the colic loops were more capacious, but there was only one true loop, the "second" being a U-shaped tract, followed by a half loop showing some individual variation.

The remainder of the large intestine, or rectal tract, extended from the colic loops to the anus, and in two specimens had a length of about 820 mm. It was not until 150 mm. beyond the loops that the contents were formed into the long pellets of typical rodent shape.

In *Neotoma* there was situated about 40 mm. posterior to the colic loops a constricted, muscular valve, heavily folded upon the ental surface. In three specimens the total length of the rectal tract was 375, 485, and 505 mm. In *Teonoma* the length of the rectal tract was 835 and 840 mm., in the case of two specimens.

Anal gland. Surrounding the rectum immediately craniad of the anus is a mass roughly spherical but slightly flattened ventrally, which in a male was 10 mm. in diameter and 9 in a female. Enclosing it is a thin layer of fibers of the M. sphincter ani internus, within which are bundles of glandular bodies, bound with fatty and connective tissue extending cranio-caudad. No sacs nor ducts within this mass could be demonstrated.

In *Neotoma* the rectal gland measured about 8 mm. in diameter. Upon either side there is a minute duct running parallel with the rectal tract, with a length of 2 or 3 mm. No direct connection with the anus or any other part could be demonstrated.

In *Teonoma* the anal gland measured 13 mm. in diameter in a male, and in two females, 11 and 10 mm. respectively. In the male, no sacs could be found in this connection, but a short distance within the glandular mass, upon either side of the ventral aspect of the females, there was a small bulbous sac, between two and three millimeters in diameter, communicating with the adjacent inner wall of the rectum by a short duct, which was demonstrable by means of a fine bristle. The normal contents of these sacs could not be ascertained in the preserved specimens, but their small size, together with the fact that they are not invested with any muscle of their own, renders it probable that the discharge of the liquid contained is not under voluntary control of the animal. The fact that they seem to be absent in the male suggests the hypothesis that they may be a secondary sexual character of the females, perhaps secreting a scent to attract the males during the breeding season.

Some discussion of variation of the alimentary tracts of related mammals with diverse food habits has been offered elsewhere (1925) by the present writer. It has now been argued that *Homodontomys* feeds chiefly upon nuts and seeds; the species of *Neotoma* investigated lives where vegetation is relatively scanty and its menu of seeds must often be supplemented with anything of an edible nature available; while *Teonoma* is largely herbivorous. The stomachs of the three subgenera reflect the effects of this fare in their degree of muscularity. *Homodontomys* has the least specialized stomach, that of *Neotoma* is considerably more muscular, though simpler in contour, while that of *Teonoma* is complex in shape and highly muscular. Size of stomach alone is of little significance, as digestion takes place in that, the small intestine and caecum.

The length of the small intestine in *Teonoma* is greatest of the three subgenera, as might be expected, but the fact that it is shortest in *Neotoma* is disconcerting. The increased diameter of the caecum may offset this, or there may be more efficient glandular action of the small intestine. There is not really sufficient difference in the caeca of the three subgenera for the drawing of significant conclusions.

But little actual digestion takes place in the rectal tract and for this reason moderate differences in food habits may affect it to a relatively slight extent. Be that as it may, the rectal tract of *Neotoma* is but slightly more than half that in the other two subgenera.

Thyroid gland. This, in *Homodontomys* and *Neotoma*,

occurs in two portions that are not joined by an isthmus. Lying one on either side of the trachea, they are small and inconspicuous and must be sought. In *Teonoma*, however, the gland is better developed, the lobes large, and the isthmus is almost as extensive antero-posteriorly as the lobes, although thinner. It is finely besprinkled with minute, black spots.

Thymus gland. This varies somewhat in size with age, as usual, but is comparatively large in the present genus, with the two lobes distinct. In a subadult though sexually mature female, each lobe measured 13 mm. in length. In a fully adult *Teonoma* it was the same size.

CHAPTER VII

UROGENITAL SYSTEM

Kidneys. In all specimens dissected the right kidney was always situated farther craniad than the left, although the amount of difference in their precise positions varied individually. There is also great individual variation in the size of the kidneys, for in two instances in each subgenus they measured: *Homodontomys,* 14 by 10 and 18 by 11 mm.; *Neotoma,* 19 by 14 and 20 by 11 mm.; *Teonoma,* 24 by 13 and 25 by 14 mm. From the medial side of the kidneys extend the ureters, passing caudad to the body of the urethra and then ventrad to their junction with the base of the bladder, upon either side. The neck of the bladder is some 12 mm. in length, and the urethral orifice in the male is near the termination of the glans penis. In the female it is upon the tip of the clitoris.[1]

MALE ORGANS

It happens that the generative organs of the males of the available specimens of *Homodontomys,* taken during August and December, and of *Teonoma* secured during August, are in a state of sexual quiescence, while those of *Neotoma albigula,* secured the middle of March, are highly active. The difference indicated in the shape of the glans penis is undoubtedly characteristic, at least for everything

[1] This term is employed only tentatively, for so far as the author is aware, the homology of this portion of the anatomy of rodents has never been established. It remains for future investigation to show whether the true clitoris has disappeared entirely and what is now termed the clitoris is merely an eminence raised about the external opening of the urethra, or whether this eminence constitutes the true clitoris, with some change of relation and function.

but relative size, and there are subgeneric or group differences in the exact shape and size of certain other parts,
as Cowper's glands and the corpora cavernosa. It is impossible, however, to distinguish with certainty which differences within the material at hand are phylogenetic and
which are due to variation in sexual activity.

The testes in the adult are partly abdominal. The
scrotal sac is therefore short and illy defined. The integument of the cranial portion is covered with short hairs,
while caudad it is practically hairless and inclined to be
wrinkled. Beneath the integument the testes are covered
by the usual diverticula of the abdominal cavity—the
tunica vaginalis—which is toughly membranous in character. They open from the cavity through the inguinal rings,
located at the lateral border of either rectus abdominis
muscle. This diverticulum is divisible into two layers or
lamina—ectalis and entalis—between which are to be
found the fibers of the M. cremaster. In young animals
the testes are entirely abdominal, but with increasing age
the two diverticula gradually develop caudad from the
inguinal rings.

The contents of the diverticulum are suspended from
its dorsal wall by a mesenteric membrane, the attachment
at the caudal end being stouter. The testis measures 10
mm. in length in the inactive *Homodontomys* and *Teonoma*,
and 17 in *Neotoma*. From its cranial portion there diverges
a bundle of several testicular veins—the pampiniform
plexus—which passes within the inguinal ring to join the
vena cava. In the drawings this bundle appears as a single
vein. Opening from the cranial portion of the testis is
also the epididymis, composed of a much-twisted canal,
with intermediate tissue. In the animals that are sexually
inactive it has shrunken to a mass probably one-fifth the
size of the testis, while in the active *Neotoma* it is fully as
large as the latter. The cranial end, or head, located for-

ward of the testis, is connected with the caudal mass of the epididymis, approximately of equal size, by a single canal, passing over the dorsum of the testis. From this caudal mass extends the vasa deferentia (together with the testicular artery), to its junction with the urethra just craniad of the bladder.

Craniad of the head of the epididymis and partly covering it is a flat mass of fat, appearing somewhat glandular in structure and possibly so in action as well. In the *Neotoma* this mass of fat is relatively small, but in the sexually in-active *Homodontomys* and *Teonoma* it is several times larger. That the fluctuation in size of this fatty tissue is correlated with sexual activity seems highly probable.

Caudad of the corpora cavernosa the penis bends craniad, and a second bend turns it caudad once more. These two portions will be referred to as the proximal and distal tracts.

The glans penis of each of the subgenera is illustrated. It is, for the most part covered with illy-defined papilla. In *Neotoma* it is roughly cylindrical, tapering gradually and terminating in a sharply-decurved, soft spine. The latter covers and partly closes the urethral orifice. Dorsad to this are two slight folds. In *Teonoma* the glans is much smaller, though whether it is so characteristically or merely because of sexual quiescence is unknown. The slight wrinkling of its tip suggests the latter explanation. It is a gradually tapering cone, ending in an acute, soft point at the tip of which there is the urethral orifice. The glans

---

Fig. 21. *A*, Urogenital organs of sexually active male *Neotoma*.

B, The same, of sexually inactive male *Homodontomys*, enlarged an equal degree.

C, Os penis of *Neotoma*.

D, Penis of *Teonoma*. *a*, glans penis, *b*, prepuce (cut); *c*, M. compressor urethrae; *d*, M. ischiocavernosus; *e*, crus of corpus cavernosum, *f*, Cowper's gland; *g*, bulb of corpus spongiosum; *h*, M. bulbocavernosus; *i*, M. sphincter ani externus; *j*, prostate gland; *k*, neck of bladder (cut); *l*, ureters; *m*, coagulating gland; *n*, seminal vesicles; *o*, fatty tissue; *p*, testis; *q*, epididy-mis; *r*, vas deferens.

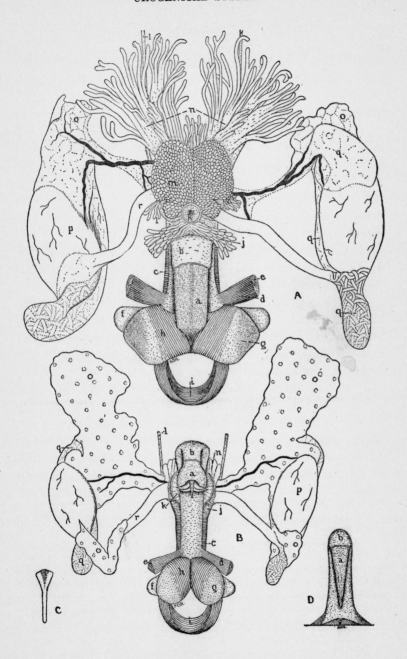

of *Homodontomys* is much shorter and has a terminal enlargement, upon which there are two lateral, curved ridges and a medial one located more dorsad, these being arranged petal-wise. In the central depression there is a long, very slender, soft spine, through which passes the urethra. In a single specimen trapped during early June, in which the genitalia are in an active state, the penis is similar, both in shape and size. In all three species first examined of the three subgenera the prepuce extended from two to five millimeters beyond the glans.

In the distal tract of *Neotoma* there is embedded an os penis 6.5 to 8 mm. in length. Distally this is spinous, but its proximal end is broad and paddle-shaped (fig. 21C). In *Teonoma* this bone is about 5.5 mm. in length, and in *Homodontomys* it is apparently absent. It is likely, however, that its size varies with age.

In order to determine whether the form of the penis is subgenerically or specifically uniform, an examination was made of the penises of the three following forms, which were the only ones of which adult males were available: *Neotoma intermedia* from Riverside, California, taken in late June when the genitalia had returned to quiescence. The prepuce extended 18 mm. beyond the glans. In the three species already discussed there were no discernible preputial glands, but in *intermedia* there was a pair of sacs nearly one millimeter in diameter and several in length upon the dorsal side of the prepuce near its termination. There was no well-defined gland in this area, but some of the tissue is probably glandular in character, as indicated by these sacs, which were filled with a white, cheesy matter in the preserved specimen. The glans was 2.5 mm. in diameter and simply cylindrical, with the urethral orifice slightly dorsad of the tip. The distal tract was 13, and the proximal, 24 mm. in length.

Neotoma micropus, from Fort Clark, Texas: date un-

known but sexually active, with seminal vesicles enlarged.
The prepuce was devoid of glandular sacs and extended
5 mm. beyond the glans. The latter was much swollen,
with a diameter of 7 mm., cylindrical and with an internal
opening 2 mm. in diameter, this enlarging with the glans
to an internal diameter of more than 3 mm. This was
filled with a transparent, jelly-like substance, and centrally within it was the spinous os penis, terminating, within
the glans, in an acute, soft spine. The distal tract was 20,
and the proximal 22 mm. in length.

Neotoma floridana rubida, from New Orleans, Louisiana,
July: sexually active, with seminal vesicles enlarged. The
penis was of the same general type as the last, but was less
extreme in development.

The conclusions reached from the examination of this
material is that the forms *rubida*, *micropus* and *albigula* of
the subgenus *Neotoma* have penises of the same general type
while those of *Neotoma intermedia*, *Homodontomys*, and
Teonoma are all different to an important degree. The
precise effect of sexual activity or inactivity upon the shape
of the glans can not be ascertained without a large series
illustrating all stages of seasonal variation in this respect.
It seems certain, however, that the glans penis will be found,
when sufficient material is available, to constitute a very
valuable character for ascertaining group relationships.

In the sexually inactive specimens the more distal portion of the corpora cavernosa could not be well defined,
as they were shrunken, pale, and without detail. In *Neotoma* they were swollen, engorged with blood and very distinct. In all specimens examined, they continued latero-
dorsad from the base of the penis to fibrous attachment
upon either ischium though much less distinctly in males
that were inactive. Almost surrounding this crus of the
corpus cavernosum is the M. ischiocavernosus. Immediately caudad is situated the large bulb (upon either

side) of what several investigators, including Osgood, have termed the corpus spongiosum, while others seem to have confused it with the corpus cavernosum. I am not aware that its true homology in this type of mammal has ever been carefully established, and as it differs in important respects from a portion of the true corpus spongiosum as usually understood, I employ the term for this structure with reservations. The tendency has too often been, while investigating the urino-genital system of mammals, to interpret all questionable structures in terms of human or feline anatomy, labelling existing glandular masses as "Cowper's glands 2 and 3," rather than to approach the subject with the thesis that such are distinct glands with special functions.

To return to the subject, the two bulbs of the corpora spongiosa vary somewhat in precise shape, and several hundred per cent in size in the specimens of the three subgenera at hand. In the active *Neotoma* the interior is spongy and highly congested, and they apparently open into the body of the urethra each by a minute duct, situated caudo-ventrad to the ducts of Cowper's gland. The medio-ventral portion of each is invested by the fibers of a muscle which may be homologous with the M. bulbocavernosus, although its nomenclature must remain a matter of doubt until the precise status of the bulbs shall have been investigated. These fibers are defined with some difficulty in animals that are sexually inactive.

The two Cowper's glands are situated craniad and slightly dorsad of the bulbs of the corpora spongiosa. In *Neotoma* they slightly exceed 5 mm. in diameter, and in the other two subgenera, are but little more than half that size. Each opens by a duct several millimeters long into the body of the urethra. The latter is invested by the M. compressor urethrae, is much the largest in the *Neotoma* at hand, and in those and the single *Homodontomys* that was sexually active, was entirely filled with a clear, jelly-like substance.

The two prostate glands are situated upon the body of the urethra immediately caudad to the neck of the bladder. In the *Homodontomys* and *Teonoma* they are but a couple of millimeters in diameter, but in *Neotoma* each takes the form of a cluster of transparent tubules of varying length, the whole extending as far as 13 mm.

In many rodents there is situated immediately craniad of the bladder a pair of glands which have usually been confused with the prostate and designated as accessory lobes of that gland. Walker (1910) established in the case of the white rat and the guinea pig, however, that this pair of glands has a special function, and termed them the coagulating glands. Their secretion coagulates the seminal fluid and is necessary to the impregnation of the female. Such coagulation is often noted by those who have trapped numbers of rodents. In *Homodontomys* and *Teonoma* these glands consist of several minute papillae, but in the sexually active *Neotoma* they have taken the form of a pair of adjacent structures consisting of a multitude of very small, much convoluted tubes, transparent and gelatinous in composition. Investigators observing these glandular masses have usually called them "prostate 2," or (as Oppel) glandula ampullarum.

The seminal vesicles in *Homodontomys* and *Teonoma* are shrunken, and while imbedded in connective tissue, take the form of a pair of small, blunt horns upon the anterior termination of the body of the urethra. They are about 8 mm. in length and appear as a pair of bundles of twisted threads. In *Neotoma* they have swollen into two clusters of transparent, occasionally branched, tubes, of slightly larger diameter than those of the coagulating glands, extending fanwise and with a total length of some 25 mm. In a single *Homodontomys* trapped in early June the seminal vesicles showed a similar seasonal development.

FEMALE ORGANS

The uteral horns of the first specimen of *Homodontomys* dissected measured 30 mm. for the right and 40 for the left. From the tip of either there extends dorsad the nor-

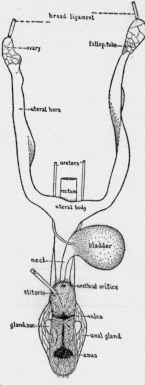

FIG. 22. Urogenital organs of female *Teonoma:* clitoris pulled forward by hook (*a*).

mal broad ligament. The ovaries in the specimens examined were inconspicuous, as were the fallopian tubes at their bases. The convergence of the uterine horns is somewhat V-shaped and the uteral body, extending caudad from their junction, measured about 30 mm. in length.

In a specimen of *Neotoma* the uteral horns both measured

about 42 mm. in length, while the convergence of the horns to the uteral body was fairly intermediate in shape between *Homodontomys* and *Teonoma*.

In *Teonoma* the right uteral horn measured 40 mm., and the left 43. Their convergence was broader and definitely U-shaped.

The vaginal opening is situated caudad to the clitoris and in normal position it is partially covered, and protected, by the latter. In no specimens examined was the vulva closed by an epithelial membrane as Miller (1895) found to be the usual condition during sexual inactivity of *Peromyscus* and some other rodents. Donaldson (1924, p. 153), however, states that "in the immature female (white rat) the vagina is closed by a membrane. This usually breaks down just before the first oestrous." That such may possibly be the case in *Neotoma* as well can not be denied.

CHAPTER VIII

OSTEOLOGY

Although in works on anatomy the osteological portion usually precedes the myological, the opposite treatment is herewith presented both for the reason that a detailed study of the bones was not made until after the dissection of the muscles had been completed, or virtually so, and because with the osteological matter is offered much information concerning the attachments of the muscles. Only such description of the bones is herewith included as was deemed necessary to the contribution. Information concerning the individual bones of the skull is especially meager, but a fuller discussion would entail much repetition of a paper already published by the author (Howell, 1924).

As with the myological portion, the osteological data are based upon skeletons of the species (*Homodontomys*) *fuscipes*, (*Neotoma*) *albigula*, and (*Teonoma*) *cinerea*. Skeletons of (*Neotoma*) *floridana rubida*, (*Neotoma*) *pennsylvanica*, and (*Neotoma*) *lepida stephensi* in a satisfactory state of articulation, and less satisfactory (*Neotoma*) *intermedia*, and (*N.*) *desertorum*, have also been studied, however, and when any of these have proved to be more extreme in any particular than the species *fuscipes*, *albigula*, and *cinerea*, the fact is mentioned.

The purpose of this osteological portion is mainly to emphasize the effects which the development, and emplacement, and attachments of the muscles, especially those of the skull and the limbs, have had upon the bones and their processes. As the attachments of many of the muscles differ in some respects from those in man and in the cat, so do the processes and other indications of muscle attachment. The majority of these, in the genus *Neotoma*, can be homologized with those of the above mammals, but for others it has been necessary to coin new terms. This has been done with as much conservatism as possible, and wherever practicable, these osteological names have been adapted to harmonize with those of the muscles which are attached to the respective parts.

SKULL

The accompanying illustrations give a better idea of the form of the skull than can a description, and complete verbal details of all the component bones is hardly necessary.

A cursory examination of skulls showing similar age development of the three subgenera compared seems to show that in *Teonoma* the rostrum is longer, the braincase is broader and shorter, and the zygomatic width is greater, than in the other two. Similarly, one gains the impression that the rostrum is longer, the braincase broader, and the zygomatic width less in *Homodontomys* than *Neotoma*.

A careful study of large series of each of these three animals would undoubtedly show trustworthy, though small, average, relative differences in measurements. But such is not the purpose of the present paper—it is for the comparison of the few specimens of each species, or rather subgenus, which one could be expected to dissect. Neither do actual differences in real size of the three animals concern us for the present purpose (osteology), and such are to be eliminated in actual comparison wherever possible.

Returning once more to apparent differences in the skull, more careful study shows that most of these are in the nature of optical illusions. After taking a dozen measurements of half a dozen skulls of adults of each of the three animals and reducing each measurement to percentage of the condylobasilar length, it is seen that the difference in relative size in the three subgenera is so slight that it probably is not

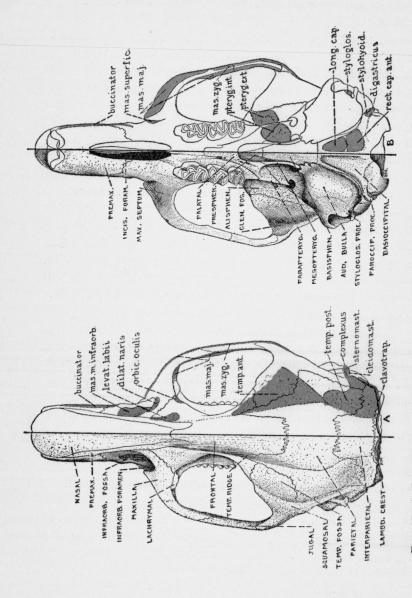

FIG. 23. *A*, Dorsal, and *B*, ventral aspects of the skull of *Teonoma*: muscle attachments indicated on right, osteological details upon the left. Origins in blue, insertions in red.

greater than is individual variation. In dorsal view, the
rostrum of *Teonoma* seems longer because of its greater
actual length, because it holds a uniform width practically
to its end, and because the anterior extension of the septa of
the maxillary processes of the zygomae are shorter: in ventral view, because the incisive foramina are longer. Actually
it seems to average only two per cent longer in this subgenus than the others. The rostrum of *Neotoma* seems
shorter than of *Homodontomys* because it tapers more
toward the tip.

The braincase of *Teonoma* is relatively the shortest. This
makes it appear broader, which illusion is strengthened by
the appearance of great width presented by the posterior portion of the zygomatic arches. This is caused chiefly by the
fact that the anterior portion of the zygoma is narrowest in
Teonoma, is slightly wider in *Neotoma*, and broadest in
Homodontomys; but relatively speaking, the difference in the
width of the braincase or in total zygomatic breadth is too
little to be taken into serious account.

The only positive indications of muscular attachments
upon the rostrum are the slight process just ventrad of the
cranio-ventral border of the infraorbital foramen, from
which originates the masseter superficialis, of equal development in all three animals, and the infraorbital fossa, situated
craniad to the foramen of the same name, from which arises
the infraorbital head of the masseter major.

As previously mentioned, the anterior portion of the
zygomatic process of the maxilla does not extend so far
craniad in *Teonoma*, and this means that the entire septum
is smaller. In the two others it is to all intents equal in size.
This indicates that the ectal portion of the masseter major
is relatively weaker in *Teonoma*, and a further indication of
this may be the narrowness in that subgenus of the anterior
portion of the zygomatic arch.

In profile the dorsal line of the skull of *Teonoma* is less

curved, with a slight depression along the anterior portion
of the cranium, which may also be present to a very slight
extent in *Homodontomys*. The dorsal line of the skull in
Neotoma is most curved. The entire skull of *Teonoma* presents a more angular appearance, chiefly due to the angularity of the zygoma and the heavy temporal ridging. The
interorbital ridging is heaviest in this animal as well, and in
fact, in all three it is better defined than is the temporal
ridging proper. The interorbital ridging is not the direct
result of any muscular stimulus. It may be a fortuitous
development—the result of crowding—or a more anterior,
secondary result of development of the temporal muscles.

The anterior division of the temporal muscle is indicated
as being appreciably strongest in *Teonoma*, and least so in
Homodontomys. This is so to an even greater extent in the
case of the posterior division of the temporal. In *Homodontomys* and *Neotoma* there is no means of distinguishing the
point where one division of the temporal ends and the other
begins, save by the slight change in direction of the temporal
ridging. In old specimens of *Teonoma*, however, the fossa
of the anterior division of the temporal is separated from
that of the posterior by a well marked ridge, running cranio-
laterad from the temporal ridging. In such animals the
lambdoidal crest is also developed to an unusual degree;
but this is also attributable to the development of certain
of the cervical muscles. Another indication of the great
strength of the temporals in *Teonoma* is the fact that they
are situated more mediad—the distance between them is
less—than in the two others, and to this extent the origins
occupy more surface. Similarly the posterior divergence

Fig. 24. Details of the skull and mandible of *Teonoma*. *A*, Lateral
aspect of the left side of skull, showing muscle attachments. *B*, Occipital
aspect of skull: muscle attachments at right, osteological details upon the
left. *C*, Medial aspect of the left side of mandible, showing muscle attachments.

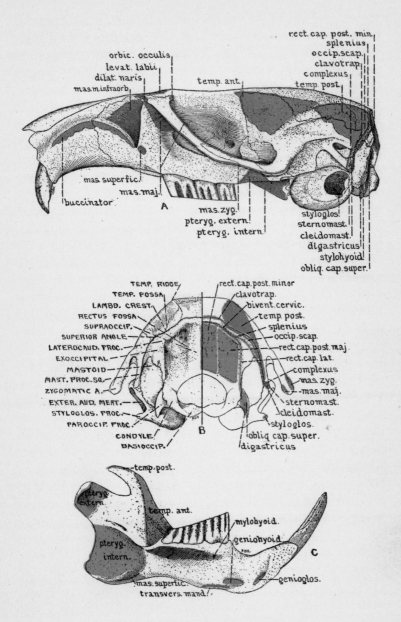

of the zygomae is more pronounced in *Teonoma*, partly to accommodate the greater bulk of temporal muscles passing within them. This detail is less pronounced in *Neotoma*, and least in *Homodontomys*. The lesser distance between the posterior portion of the temporal ridges in *Teonoma* crowds the interparietal to a greater extent, and as age increases this exhibits a tendency to change shape from roughly rectangular to more of the form of the section through a truncated cone.

The braincase or cranium proper is relatively shortest in *Teonoma* because its cranio-lateral borders do not slope so gradually from the zygomatic arches towards the interorbital. Judging by the dorsal aspect of the cranium, one expects the capacity of the braincase to be relatively least in this subgenus, but this seems to be the case to too slight a degree to be of much importance. After stuffing the olfactory fossae and the cranial foramina with cotton, the braincases of the skulls studied were filled with number ten shot, and the cube root of the number of these was found, so as to render the item more comparable with linear measure. The percentage of this, as compared to the condylobasilar length, was then computed. The relative difference in brain capacity between the three subgenera is indicated as being rather insignificant (about 18.2 per cent for *Neotoma*, 17.7 for *Homodontomys*, and 17 for *Teonoma*). It is thus seen that *Teonoma* does have a smaller capacity, although to a slighter degree than a visual inspection suggests.

According to the above figures, *Teonoma* has the smallest braincase, relative to length of skull, and *Neotoma* the largest. The latter circumstance is unexpected, although with a larger series the positions of *Homodontomys* and *Neotoma* might be reversed in this respect, for, it seems to be a fact, broadly speaking, that mammals with the largest temporal muscles have the smallest brains (see Anthony, 1903), and that a more extensive muscular covering inhibits by just so much the growth of the bones concerned. In this respect it is significant that the largest *Teonoma* among the large series available, with condylo-basilar length of 54.6 mm. and temporal ridges but 3.6 mm. apart, has a brain capacity of but 14.7 per cent, figured by the above formula.

Turning to the ventral aspect of the skull, it is found that *Teonoma* has the longest diastema in comparison to its condylo-basilar length (34.2 per cent), and *Neotoma* the shortest (30.2, with *Homodontomys* 31.3). One point influencing the length of the diastema in the last is the fact that either the upper molar row is situated more caudad than in the other two, or what is more likely, the zygomatic processes of the maxillae are located a trifle more craniad. There is very slight relative difference in the length of the incisive foramina compared to the extent of the diastema. The nasal arteries and nasopalatine nerves passing through these foramina are small, and hence the large size of the foramina and their variation in different mammals seems due entirely to Jacobson's organs, of the nasal passages.

The zygomatic processes of the maxillae, in comparison with the posterior portion of the zygomatic arches, are relatively broadest in *Homodontomys*, less so in *Neotoma*, and least in *Teonoma*. Another fact of significance is that in the last-mentioned genus the bony septum of the zygomatic process of the maxilla is narrowest, while in the other two it is about equal in width. These circumstances indicate that at least the greater portion of the masseter muscle is stronger, or at least relatively larger, in *Homodontomys*, less so in *Neotoma*, and least in *Teonoma*. Osteological differences in the posterior portion of the zygomatic arch are not of such a character as to enable one to judge regarding any subgeneric variation in the development of the fibers of the muscles originating therefrom.

There is much individual and some specific difference in

the shape of the palate and the precise conformation of the mesopterygoid plates, but not to an extent easily expressed by words. *Teonoma* usually has a slightly defined, medial spine to the palate. There are also differences in the shape of the audital bullae, those of *Teonoma* being least globular, but the variation in relative size is slight. The styloglossal process upon the inferior border of the auditory meatus is well developed in all three, perhaps best so in *Neotoma*, but the latter assertion is not corroborated by any appreciable difference in the muscle itself. The pterygoid fossae are narrowest in *Homodontomys* and deepest in *Neotoma*, indicating stronger internal pterygoid muscles in the latter animal. There is equal development of the fossa upon either side of the basioccipital bone, from which originate the longis capitis and rectus capitis anterior muscles, and of the paroccipital processes. The latter serve for attachment of the obliquus capitis superior, stylohyoid, and digastric muscles, and especially in view of differences obtaining in the last, these processes might be expected to exhibit greater variation.

So many muscles are attached to the rear of the skull that the occipital varies individually in a very complex manner, and perhaps the only safe subgeneric statement to make is that in *Teonoma* the occipital surface is more prone to exhibit an anterior inclination. The reason for this in the present animal is obscure. In rodents this is popularly accepted as a fossorial character, but as far as known *Teonoma* is even less given to burrowing than are other wood rats that do not show this development.

The angularity and definition of the processes, especially the medial spine, of the occipital increase with age, as is to be expected, but the depth of the rectus fossae varies more with the individual than with age. There undoubtedly occur indications of differences in the development of the cervical muscles, but they are so inextricably interwoven that it seems unsafe to treat them in detail.

In *Neotoma* the prelambdoidal fenestration of the squamosal is considerably the smallest, and this either may indicate that the mastoid process of the squamosal is weaker, or it may be fortuitous as far as muscular development is

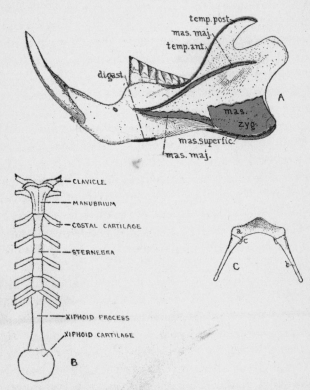

Fig. 25. *A*, Lateral aspect of left mandible of *Teonoma*, showing areas of muscle attachments. *B*, Sternum of *Teonoma*. *C*, Hyoid of *Homodontomys*, showing (*a*) body, (*b*) greater cornu, and (*c*) lesser cornu.

concerned. This mastoid process is heavier in *Teonoma*, which should indicate greater strength of the attached sternomastoid, cleidomastoid, and complexus muscles.

The differences exhibited by the mandibles of the three animals are relatively slight. In *Teonoma* the lower jaws appear to be slightly more massive, relatively speaking; but this may be only an optical illusion due to their greater size. In that subgenus the coronoid process, upon which are inserted the temporal, is definitely more robust, thus conforming to other indications of the greater strength of this muscle in the animal in question. The angular process, upon which is inserted chiefly the internal pterygoid muscle, is shortest in *Homodontomys*, conforming to the narrower pterygoid fossa of this subgenus. Both the dorsal and ventral masseteric ridges are equally well developed in all three animals, their definition increasing with age. The same may be said respecting the definition of the insertion of the masseter superficialis upon the ventral border of the angular process.

The symphysis menti is movable as usual in the present genus, and the two halves of the mandible are connected by tough, elastic tissue. The fibers of the transversus mandibularis help to control their action and to lend additional strength to their connection. As the muscle is thus of importance, its attachment is marked upon either side by a slight fossa, perhaps most extensive in *Teonoma* and least so in *Homodontomys*.

To recapitulate, direct indications upon the bones of the head of comparative differences in the muscular development of the three animals is as follows: The temporal muscles are most powerful in *Teonoma* and least so in *Homodontomys*. The infraorbital head of the masseter is a trifle the largest in *Teonoma* and smallest in *Homodontomys*, but probably the difference is not sufficient to be of functional importance. The ectal and ental divisions of the masseter major are apparently greatest in *Homodontomys*, and least in *Teonoma*. The internal pterygoid muscles are a trifle smaller in *Homodontomys* than in the other two subgenera. One or more of the three muscles attached to the mastoid process of the squamosal is strongest in *Teonoma*, and reference to the myology shows that this is the case with the sterno- and cleidomastoids.

A summary of the cranial osteological differences, some of which are obscurely or not at all related to the musculature of the three animals, is as follows: The anterior extension of the infraorbital plate of the maxillary process is shortest in *Teonoma;* the dorsal line in profile is straightest in *Teonoma;* most curved in *Neotoma;* the interorbital ridges, separated by a sulcus, are heaviest in *Teonoma;* the audital bullae are least globular in the same subgenus: the posterior portion of the zygomatic arches are relatively most flaring in *Teonoma* and least so in *Homodontomys;* the interpterygoid fossa is broadest in *Neotoma,* and the pterygoid fossae narrowest in *Homodontomys;* in *Teonoma* the palatals extend quite to the basi- and presphenoids, while in the other two animals they do not, thus forming wide vacuities within this portion of the pterygoid fossa—an excellent subspecific character, but one which does not prove to be subgenerically uniform; in *Teonoma* the post-palatal foramen consists of a slight slit, in *Neotoma* it is more truly a foramen and in *Homodontomys* it is largest.

Teeth

The incisors are a trifle broader and heavier in *Teonoma* than in the other two animals. As is always the case in rodents, they grow from persistent pulps throughout the life of the individual.

The molariform teeth are moderately brachyodont, or short crowned, but to a less extent than in such a genus as *Peromyscus,* in this respect being fairly intermediate between the latter and such an animal as *Evotomys.*

The length of the tooth row, as figured in percentage of the condylobasilar length, is far more variable individually and with age than subgenerically. In fact, this is the case to such a degree that it can not be determined whether there be an insignificant subgeneric variation or not. The maxillary tooth rows are more nearly parallel in *Teonoma* than in the other two, but to too slight an extent to constitute a good subgeneric criterion. The molars are a shade the broadest in *Homodontomys*, and narrowest in *Teonoma*. The third upper molar is slightly smaller in *Neotoma* than in the other two, and this is stressed by Goldman (1910) as a good character by which *Homodontomys* may be separated from *Neotoma;* but I consider this difference also too slight to be of much subgeneric importance.

Each molariform tooth row consists of three teeth. The

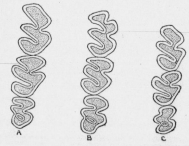

Fig. 26. Enamel pattern of right upper series of molariform teeth of A, *Homodontomys*, B, *Teonoma*, and C, *Neotoma*, selected to show the same stage of wear of the third tooth.

first or anteriormost of the upper molars has three enamel spaces, formed by two outer and an inner reentrant angle. In addition, the antero-internal enamel face may or may not be indented to a variable degree. The second molar, although of somewhat different configuration from the first, also has three enamel spaces, two outer and an inner reentrant angle. The same description applies to the third molar as well, although this again differs in shape from, and is smaller than, the other two. In *Homodontomys*, a secondary reentrant angle of the postero-external angle often exhibits a tendency to bisect the middle enamel space. This trait is given by Goldman (1910) as a subgeneric character, but it is quite variable and does not seem entirely reliable.

In this postero-external reentrant angle is first found, in the case of animals in the prime of adulthood, a development which may occur in practically every other angle as senility of the individual advances. This consists of a segregation of the apex of the angle into an island of dentine entirely surrounded by enamel (see fig. 26), and the final, though not immediate, obliteration of all signs of the angle as such upon the external, or lateral, surface of the tooth. This is caused by the fact that the reentrant angles extend deeper vertically in the central portion of the teeth than along the margins, so that after the teeth are much worn, the bases of the angles are obliterated sooner than the apices.

The first of the lower molars has three enamel spaces, and normally two inner and two outer reentrant angles. In some individuals the antero-internal angle is lightly defined, and an accessory reentrant angle may be indicated upon the antero-internal border of the first enamel space. The second molar also has three enamel spaces, two internal and two external reentrant angles. The postero-external one of the latter is the first to become isolated by wear. The third molar is formed of two enamel spaces and a reentrant angle upon either side, the external one of which is the first to become isolated by wear. The third molars, both above and below, are cut much later than the remainder of the cheek teeth.

HYOID

The hyoid bone consists of a transverse body, with a slight, mediocranial projection, two greater cornua, which are a trifle shorter than the transverse measurement of the body, extending latero-caudo-dorsad, and two lesser cornua located at the junctions of the greater cornua with the body.

The lesser occur as very small processes at this point and are so poorly developed that it is doubtful whether their ossification is complete.

The hyoid of *Teonoma* is slightly the largest.

VERTEBRAL COLUMN

The number of skeletons available are satisfactory for the purposes of the present paper; but very few of them are perfect in all respects. Some are without skulls, several without feet, and others are disarticulated in varying degree. Neither are the measurements absolutely trustworthy, for the backbones are curved into various positions. In addition, the given length of any class of vertebrae, as the lumbar series, is not the real, but the apparent length, as measured upon the middorsal line of the visible portions of the vertebrae concerned.

There are but three skeletons of *Homodontomys*, three of *Neotoma*, and two of *Teonoma* in such position as to render the taking of vertebral measurements entirely satisfactory. For our purpose the measurement of total length is not as desirable as that of the skeletal body length, comprising the sum of the cervical, thoracic, lumbar, and sacral vertebrae series.

CERVICAL VERTEBRAE

There are seven cervical vertebrae, as usual, including atlas and axis. In *Homodontomys* this series has a length of 20, 18.4, and 18 mm. respectively, or 13.7, 13.3, and 13.7 per cent of the vertebral body length. In *Neotoma* these figures are 13.9, 14, and 13.3 mm., or 12.7, 13.2, and 12.6 per cent of the body length; and in *Teonoma*, they are 20.4 and 17.7 mm., or 13.9 and 12.9 per cent. (In *Neotoma l. stephensi* this percentage is 15.5, and in *N. f. rubida*, 15.1.)

The atlas, articulating with the skull, is moderately

heavy, 12 to 14 mm. in width, 8 to 9 in height, and does not
vary appreciably in form. Salient points of the atlas are
the two transverse processes, the spine of the ventral arch,
and the spine of the dorsal arch. The ventral spine serves
chiefly as a point of attachment for the longus colli. Other
muscles attached to the atlas are the atlanto scapularis,
rectus capitis anterior, longus atlantis, recti capitis posterior minor and lateralis, and obliqui capitis superior and
inferior.

The axis is characterized by a well developed odontoid
process extending craniad upon its ventral arch, transverse
processes smaller than those of any other cervical vertebra,
and a very high, broad (in a sagittal direction), dorsal spine.
The atlas varies from 8.3 to 8.9 mm. in breadth, and 9.2 to
10 mm. in height. The spine in *Neotoma* is a trifle narrower
and higher in proportion, and its cranial part is relatively
lower in *Teonoma*, possibly indicating a weaker development in the latter animal of one of the capiti muscles. To
the axis are attached the biventer cervices, spinalis dorsi,
rectus capitis posterior major, obliquus capitis inferior, and
very possibly a few fibers of some of the adjoining muscles.

The second to fifth, inclusive, cervical vertebrae are
characterized by the breadth and flatness of the ventral
aspect. The pre- and postzygapophyses are present in the
second to seventh cervicals and of the usual form. In these
the length of the so-called transverse processes gradually
increases progressively in caudal sequence. They are single
—not branched—and extending first ventrad and then
caudad from the sixth is a well-developed inferior lamella.
The longus colli muscle extends both ways from this process
and may be chiefly responsible for the variation which it
exhibits, but the latter is believed to be phylogenetic as well.
It is a trifle the best developed in *Homodontomys*, and perhaps least so in *Neotoma*. The dorsal spines of the fourth to
seventh cervicals are poorly defined and that of the third

slightly better so. The third vertebra has a width of about 10 mm., the seventh 13 or 14, and they average about 6.5 mm. in height.

The other muscles that are with certainty attached to the five posterior, cervical vertebrae are the scalenus, longus capitis, longus colli, longus atlantis, and levator scapulae upon transverse processes, and complexus, spinalis dorsi, and transversospinales to other portions. In addition, other muscles which are considered as arising from the middorsal line most certainly influence the length of the spines of all the vertebrae concerned.

Thoracic vertebrae

There are thirteen pairs of ribs in the genus *Neotoma* arising from the same number of thoracic vertebrae. In the adults available the visible portion of the thoracic series, measured upon the dorsum between the spines, is 51.5, 50, and 45.4 mm. in *Homodontomys*, or 35.3, 36.2, and 34.5 per cent of the vertebral body length. In *Neotoma* the figures are 40, 40, and 41 mm., or 36.7, 38, and 38.8 per cent of the body length. In *Teonoma* they are 55 and 51 mm., or 37.4 and 37.2 per cent of the body length. (In *N. p. pennsylvanica* this percentage is 40.)

The dorsal aspect of the first thoracic vertebra is typically similar in the majority of cases to the characteristic form of the cervical vertebra, but in a single specimen of *Homodontomys* the spine is about 3 mm. in length—as long as that of the fourth. The spine of the second vertebra is much longer than any of the others, although this character varies both individually and with age. It may reach a length of over 8 mm., or be but half that height. In *Homodontomys* and *Neotoma* the spines of the remaining thoracics are practically uniform in height, measuring three or four millimeters; but in *Teonoma* the third and fourth are longer, being graduated in decreasing size caudad from the second

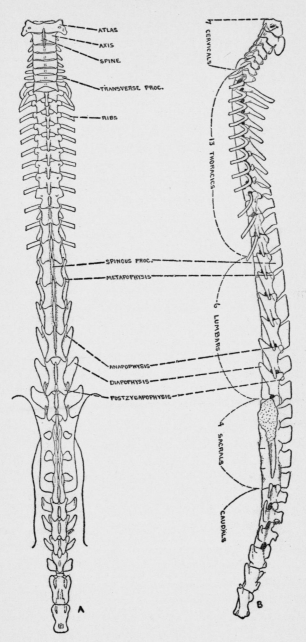

FIG. 27. Body vertebrae and first six caudal vertebrae of *Teonoma*. *A*, Dorsal aspect. *B*, Left lateral aspect.

vertebra. As far caudad as the ninth (inclusive), or in two *Homodontomys* the tenth, thoracic vertebra the spines are relatively slender, and show a definite inclination caudad. Posterior to this, the remaining thoracic spines are of the lumbar type, being very broad in a sagittal direction. In man there is a somewhat similar change in the shape of the spines posterior to the tenth thoracic vertebra, and posterior to the ninth in the cat, although the tenth and eleventh are intermediate in form. The point upon the vertebral column at which the inclination of the spines changes indicates the center of motion and seems to be influenced chiefly by the spinalis dorsi, although other factors are undoubtedly involved to some extent.

The thoracic vertebrae as far caudad as the tenth (inclusive) have single, lateral processes on either side above the ribs, which may be termed transverse processes solely by reason of their general position, although I am not aware that their precise homology with what are herein termed the transverse processes of the cervical series has ever been established in a thoroughly satisfactory manner. Each vertebra has also a pair of postzygapophyses, but in the first nine of this series these are hardly developed as true processes.

The transverse processes of the tenth thoracic are broader in a sagittal direction, while in the eleventh, these have separated to form the met- and anapophyses (see fig. 27). The former, in this vertebra, are situated more dorsad than the transverse processes of the tenth. Progressively caudad, each of the processes thereafter increases in size. The postzygapophyses, beginning with the tenth thoracic, also increase progressively in size in ratio with the metapophyses. The eleventh thoracic is the narrowest of all the body vertebrae, and each one succeedingly caudad is a trifle broader.

The muscles more intimately concerned with the thoracic
series of vertebrae are the longus colli, biventer cervices,
longissimus cervicis and dorsi, quadratus lumborum, transversospinales, and possibly the complexus. A reason was
especially sought for the great length of the spine of the
second thoracic—a character found in many rodents—but
without success. The rhomboideus posticus originates
chiefly from this spine, being the only muscle which does so;
but in the opinion of the writer this is hardly sufficient to
account fully for its development. Similarly, no convincing
muscular reason was encountered for the change in form of
the lateral processes upon the more caudal vertebrae of the
thoracic series. As previously indicated, the interrelationship of the muscle fibers of the long system are often so
extremely complex and difficult of precise definition that one
is inclined to be conservative in arriving at conclusions.

LUMBAR VERTEBRAE

Six lumbar vertebrae are found in the genus *Neotoma*. In
Homodontomys the series measures 46 mm. in all three specimens, or 31.5, 33.3, and 35 per cent of the vertebral body
length. In *Neotoma* these figures are 35.3, 33, and 32 mm.,
or 32.4, 31.3, and 30.3 per cent of the body length. In
Teonoma they are 45 and 44 mm., or 30.6 and 32.1 per cent
of the body length.

In most respects the lumbars are very similar to the last
thoracic vertebrae—in processes and the spine—but each
grows successively larger than the one cranially preceding.
In *Homodontomys* the postzygapophyses of the last, and in
Neotoma and *Teonoma* of the last two, are appreciably
smaller than of the others. Upon the first lumbar vertebra
a small diapophysis is first found (see fig. 27). The transverse width between the terminations of these processes is
about 7 mm. In each lumbar succeeding, these are pro-

gressively much larger, until the width between their points at the sixth may be as much as 17 mm. (in a very old individual of *Teonoma*). As suggested, their size increases much with age. This sixth is the only vertebra of the lumbar series in which there is practically no anapophysis. In none of the vertebrae does a prezygapophysis occur as a true process.

Jayne (1898) designates the diapophyses as "transverse processes," which seems unfortunate, for they are not homologous with what he (and I) have termed the transverse processes of the more cranial of the thoracic series. His "mammillary process" and "accessory process" are also less desirable terms than the corresponding metapophysis and anapophysis.

The definition of the ventral ridge or hypapophysis upon the body of the lumbar vertebrae of *Homodontomys* increases progressively from barely perceptible upon the first to very sharp upon the sixth; but this is the case to a lesser extent in *Neotoma* and *Teonoma*.

The multifidis spinae is situated between the spines and the metapophyses, while the muscles most intimately concerned with the diapophyses are the longissimus dorsi, quadratus lumborum and psoas magnus. The psoas minor and flexor caudae longus also have attachment upon these vertebrae.

SACRAL VERTEBRAE

The four sacral vertebrae have a total length in *Homodontomys* of 28.2, 23.5, and 22 mm., or 19.3, 17, and 16.7 per cent of the vertebral body length. In *Neotoma* these figures are 20, 18.5, and 19 mm., or 18.3, 17.6, and 18 per cent. In *Teonoma* they are 26.5 and 24 mm., or 18.2 and 17.5 per cent of the body length.

In the case of the animals under discussion these vertebrae

form a solid unit through the fusion of their diapophyses. and to some extent of the other processes as well, except in a single specimen of *Homodontomys* in which the fourth resembles the first caudal vertebra and is similarly articulated. In *Neotoma lepida stephensi*, and to a lesser extent in the only *Neotoma pennsylvanica* available, the diapophyses of the sacrals are not completely fused with their neighbors.

Anapophyses as such are lacking in the sacral series. The diapophyses of the first are prolonged and very stout, and with the cranial half of the diapophyses of the second, articulate with the ilia. The metapophyses of the first sacral vertebra are large, but those of the remainder, together with their postzygapophyses, are much reduced in size and are insignificant. The sacral series averages a trifle broader, perhaps, in *Teonoma*, but the individual is greater than the subgeneric variation in this respect. The shortest interilial measurement at the point of articulation varies from 8.5 to nearly 12 mm. The breadth across the diapophyses is from 2 to 3.5 mm. greater in the posterior than the anterior portion of the series in old *Homodontomys* and *Neotoma*, while in *Teonoma* the two measurements are approximately equal. These points are doubtless influenced partly by variation in the development of the multifidis spinae and caudal extension of the longissimus dorsi, although they undoubtedly also reflect certain pelvic differences. Other muscles definitely concerned with the sacral vertebrae are the medial and lateral extensors, and the long and short flexors, of the tail, and to a much lesser extent, the pyriformis and biceps femoris anticus.

CAUDAL VERTEBRAE

The caudal vertebrae vary in number with the individual. In the articulated skeletons at hand there are 31 caudals in four specimens of *Homodontomys* and 28 in one; in *Neotoma*, 28 caudals in three individuals; in two *Teonoma* there are 26 vertebrae in one, and probably 25 in the other. Of the latter, the tail is slightly damaged, and it is believed that but one vertebra is missing. In two specimens of *Homodontomys* the caudal series measures 196 and 215 mm., or 134 and 156 per cent of the vertebral body length. In *Neotoma* these figures are 148, 130, and 137 mm., or 136, 124, and 129 per cent of the body. In *Teonoma* the measurements are 175 and 166 mm., or both 119 per cent of the body length. These vertebrae are most robust in *Homodontomys* and lightest in *Neotoma*, conforming to expectations in consideration of different life habits.

It is individually variable whether the first two or first three caudal vertebrae are the only ones of this series whose spines extend farther dorsad than the other processes. These decrease in height progressively in caudal sequence. Similarly with the diapophyses, which are a trifle the largest in *Homodontomys* and smallest in *Neotoma*. Those of the first caudal are practically as broad as in the sacrals, but in each succeeding vertebra they are smaller. In the fifth they are very small, and in *Homodontomys* only there is situated directly caudad to them a pair of miniature replicas. The anapophyses are also well developed in the first five vertebrae, being successively and progressively smaller caudad. In reality transition from the first caudal vertebra to the form typical of those of the middle tail is quite gradual; but it can be said that the first five are of the proximal type, and the remainder of the distal. Each of the latter has a pair of metapophyses in the form of tubercles, a mid-dorsal ridge terminating caudad in a pair of small postzygapophyses that are practically coalesced, a lateral ridge upon either side that consists of modified di- and anapophyses, and ventrad, a pair of hypapophyses which are prolonged caudad to form a single mid-ventral ridge. Chevron bones occur caudad at least to within six vertebrae of the tail tip. No definite statement in regard to their number can be ventured, for if the skeleton has been well cleaned, many of them will have been lost, while if poorly cleaned, the smaller ones can not be made out with certainty.

The muscles concerned with the caudal vertebrae are the lateral and medial extensors, the external abductor and the short flexor. As the last two of these extend but as far as the fifth vertebrae, and are the only ones which do so, they are evidently chiefly responsible for the development upon these only of diapophyses of noteworthy length. Both *Homodontomys* and *Teonoma* are more scansorial, and therefore both employ the tail as an equilibrator. The bushy tail of *Teonoma* offers more resistance to the air, and therefore, the more terete tail of *Homodontomys* must be more strongly waved about in order to secure the same degree of equilibrium for its owner. The development of the first five caudal vertebrae shows that abduction and flexion of the tail is more efficient in the latter subgenus, as might be expected. Also according with this line of reasoning is the fact that *Neotoma*, which climbs less and has less need for an efficient balancer, has tail bones and processes that are somewhat the lightest.

Attention should be called to the fact that in the genus *Neotoma* there is no definite elevation of the spines of the vertebrae at any point posterior to the second or third thoracic. Special length of the spines at any point is an indication of particular strength in that region and is a character exhibited by certain mammals fitted for a particular mode of living. In this respect, therefore, the genus is indicated as being definitely generalized in development.

THORAX

STERNUM

The sternum consists of the manubrium, the body, composed of four sternebrae, and the xiphoid process. In a single *Homodontomys*—the same in which the fourth sacral vertebra was not ankylosed with the third—the third and fourth sternebrae are completely fused. In three *Homodontomys* the length of the sternum is 42.6, 37.3, and 34.8 mm., or respectively 29.2, 27, and 26 per cent of the vertebral body length. In *Neotoma* these figures are 32, 31.5, and 34.8 mm. or 29.4, 30, and 33 per cent. In *Teonoma* it measures 46.8 and 43 mm., or 31.8 and 31.4 per cent of the body length.

The manubrium is centrally indented craniad, T-shaped, with a body and two lateral processes upon the cranial end. The body is longest in *Homodontomys* and much the shortest in *Neotoma*, although there is considerable individual variation in this respect. The manubrial processes are, however, largest in *Teonoma*. The first ribs articulate by facets in the angle between the processes and body, and the second, in a similar manner laterad upon the caudal end of the body. The muscles most intimately connected with the manubrium are the sternofascialis in *Homodontomys* only, and the rectus abdominis and pectoralis superficialis in all three subgenera. If there are any muscular stimuli that have directly affected the subgeneric difference in the manubrium they are obscure.

The first sternebra is a trifle shorter than the manubrium, and each of the others is slightly shorter than the one next craniad. They are a trifle the longest in *Teonoma*, and perhaps shortest in *Neotoma*, while the posterior ones are heaviest in the former subgenus. The facets upon the caudal portion of each are attached respectively to the third, fourth, fifth, and sixth ribs, and the seventh are also attached to the ventral portion of the fourth sternebra medio-caudad of the sixth costal cartilages. The muscles arising upon this portion of the midventral line doubtless have some effect upon the sternebrae, but the stimuli affecting them are regarded as being more mechanical than myological, through the influences of the ribs.

The length of the xiphoid process is individually variable, and it seems to be least robust in *Neotoma*. It extends caudad from its articulation with the fourth sternebra, and upon its caudal border is attached the thin, disk-like, xiphoid cartilage, usually largest in *Teonoma*. The muscles chiefly concerned with the xiphoid process are the pectoralis profundus and the sternocostales.

Ribs

There are thirteen pairs of ribs attached to the costal facets of their respective thoracic vertebrae, and they are considerably flattened upon the cranial and caudal surfaces. They increase in length to the ninth, after which this measurement decreases. Cartilages extend from the sternal ends, and the first seven of these are in turn attached to the sternum. The cartilage of each of the others successively caudad is attached to the cartilage of the rib next craniad, except the thirteenth, and probably occasionally the twelfth, which is free. The thoracic capacity, or space inclosed by the ribs, is relatively somewhat greater in *Teonoma*.

EXTREMITIES

Pectoral girdle

The true affinity of the pectoral and pelvic girdles is usually considered as being with the vertebral column rather than with the ribs. The girdles are so intimately concerned with most of the myological functions of the limbs, however, that for convenience they will be discussed with the respective appendages articulate with them.

Clavicle. The clavicle is attached by connective tissue to the dorsal border of the lateral process of the manubrium, and by its opposite end to the acromion of the scapula. It is curved in two planes and flattened upon its scapular end. In the specimens at hand it forms the following proportion of the skeletal body lengths: in two specimens of *Homodontomys*, 11.8 and 12 per cent; in two of *Neotoma*, 12.7 and 13.2 per cent; and in two of *Teonoma*, 12.6 and 13.4 per cent. The slight processes dorsad near the scapular end and ventrad near the sternal end seem not to have been caused directly by muscular action, but rather by the adjoining articulations. The muscles chiefly concerned with the scapular end of the clavicle are the clavotrapezius, cleidomastoid, and subclavius, and with the medial end, the pectoralis profundus and clavo-acromiodeltoid.

Scapula. Real length of the scapula, as well as of most other bones, is so variable with age that this item should receive but little consideration. Its length relative to functional arm length is more significant, however, but is found to have considerable individual variation. In *Homodontomys* this figure varies from 42 to 48 per cent, with an average of 45; in *Neotoma* it is from 42.7 to 44.8, averaging 44 per cent; and in *Teonoma* the variation is from 42 to 47.6 per cent, with 45.2 as an average. There is a tendency for the scapula to be slightly smaller in relation to arm length in the case of younger animals. The width of the scapula, compared with its length, shows slight variation in *Homodontomys* (from 45 to 47 per cent) and *Neotoma* (43.5 to 45 per cent), but more in *Teonoma* (44 to 50 per cent). There is great individual variation in the exact form of the vertebral border of the scapula, chiefly in the region of the coracovertebral angle.

The lateral surface of the scapula is divided into two parts by the spine. Craniad to the latter is the supraspinous fossa, and caudad, the infraspinous fossa. The axillary border of the latter is considerably raised, probably partly by the influence of the triceps longus and the teres minor originating upon its border, and possibly by the juxtaposition of the teres major. The coracovertebral portion of the supraspinous fossa is usually slightly raised, but is perfectly flat in some cases. The teres major originates upon the gleno-vertebral angle, but it has no appreciable effect upon it. The same may be said of the occipitoscapularis, arising from the vertebral border of the supraspinous fossa, and the rhomboideus posticus, in almost the same relation to the infraspinous fossa. From the remainder of these two fossae originate respectively the two muscles after which they are named. The scapula narrows ventrad to form the neck, the cranial border of which is known as the supra-scapular notch. Upon the ventral portion of this originates the omohyoid muscle.

The spine of the scapula occupies a position roughly central upon its lateral surface. At its vertebral termination there is a small triangular area over which passes the apo-neurosis of the trapezius. As it passes cranio-ventrad the spine is bent caudo-ventrad, which change in direction is influenced by the pull of the spinodeltoid attached to the caudo-ventral border, and the acromiotrapezius upon the cranio-dorsal border. It should be noted that the stress of the latter is against the inclination of the spine. In addition, the spinotrapezius is inserted upon the dorsal third or fourth of the lateral border of the spine. Upon the remainder of the more dorsal aspect originates a separate head of the supra-spinatus muscle. The border of the spine ends ventrad in the metacromion, a process formed by the sharp bending of the spinal border, apparently influenced by the spino-deltoid, atlanto-scapularis, and possibly by the teres minor beneath it. The spinal border then passes dorsad and slightly mediad, ending in the acromion. Upon this ventral border between the metacromion and acromion is part of the origin of the clavo-acromiodeltoid. The latter muscle, and articulation of the acromion with the clavicle, results in some individual variation in the precise shape of this process and its border, but in nothing that can be considered as sub-generic. The ventral third or less of the spine is free from

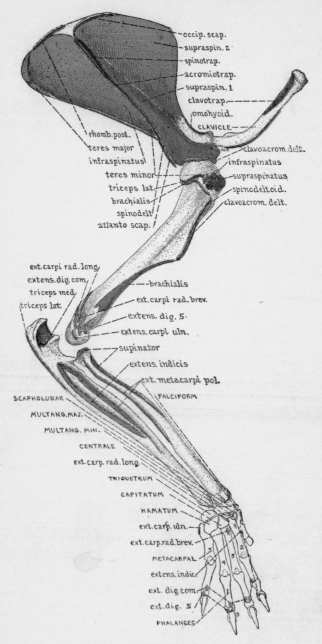

FIG. 28. Lateral aspect of right fore limb and shoulder of *Teonoma* showing muscle attachments (origins in blue, insertions in red).

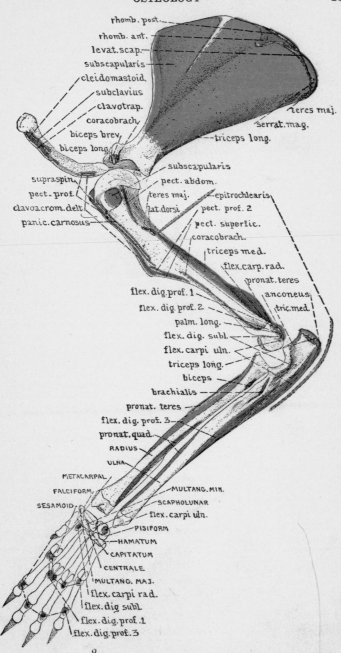

FIG. 29. Medial aspect of right fore limb and shoulder of *Teonoma*, showing muscle attachments.

medial connection with the remainder of the scapula, and the termination of its juncture with the latter constitutes the spinal notch.

The subscapularis arises from almost the entire medial surface of the scapula. The plane of the latter is interrupted by the subscapular ridge, the definition of which varies individually, and the subspinal fossa. Upon either side of the former arises one of the two main divisions of the subscapular muscle. The form of the subspinal fossa is apparently a mechanical result of the presence of the spine upon the lateral surface. The insertion of the rhomboideus anticus exhibits a tendency to follow the subspinal fossa for a short distance along its dorsal termination. This same insertion, together with that of the rhomboideus posticus situated more dorsad, extends along the vertebral border of the scapula for a short distance. Upon the medial border of the glenovertebral angle are inserted the levator scapulae and serratus magnus, and a small portion of the teres major also takes origin from this surface. The rate of ossification of the border of the scapula at the glenovertebral angle is slow, and this line of ossification, of variable extent, remains most clearly visible in *Teonoma*. Any variation in the remainder of this portion of the scapula is individual, however, rather than subgeneric.

The triceps longus originates upon the ventral third of the axillary border of the medial scapula. From the constricted neck, the slightly enlarged head of the scapula extends cranio-ventrad. Upon this is the glenoid cavity, articulating with the humerus, and ventro-caudad, the caudal process of the head. It is best developed in *Teonoma*, due probably to the larger head of the humerus in that animal. Upon the dorso-cranial border of the head is the coracoid process, rather slender and inclined first mediad and then ventrad. Upon its tip originate the coracobrachialis and biceps brevis, and from its base, the biceps longus. This, too, is best developed in *Teonoma*, but as none of these three muscles was noted as relatively stronger in that animal, the development of this process may well be due to some difference in the average of the kind of work performed by the muscles in question.

ANTERIOR LIMB

In analyzing the actions of the limbs, it will be seen that the scapula plays a considerable mechanical part in the activities of the fore leg. It may be thrust forward or backward as occasion demands, this, in reality, adding functional length to the real length of the leg proper. This in some degree compensates for the (usually) greater length of the hind leg in mammals with its immovable pelvis; or if one prefer, the reverse may be stated. At any rate, if one is to be precise, the thesis must be accepted that the scapula is in some degree a functional portion of the thoracic limb. It is equally true that the immovable pelvis can not be considered as having the same relation to the hind limb.

In comparing functional length of the fore and hind legs, therefore, the measurement should be taken from the hip joint for the latter, and for the former, really from some indeterminate position upon the scapula, the exact point depending entirely upon the importance of this segment in the economy of movement. The importance and degree of such movements naturally vary much in different mammals, and any arbitrary point selected for beginning this projected measurement of functional length of fore leg would vary with each investigator, and to a corresponding degree would be valueless.

Under present technique, therefore, the inclusion of any fractional measurement of the scapula in a consideration of the functional length of the fore limb is not practicable, however desirable it may be from a theoretical viewpoint. Perhaps this really is not of great import, for what is chiefly

needed in a consideration of functional morphology of mammals of high specialization is merely a standard of comparison between the fore and hind limbs as a whole and their
several segments, as well as of various other parts of the body.

For practical purposes, then, the functional length of the
fore limb should be considered as the distance from the
scapular-humeral joint to the ground when the animal is in

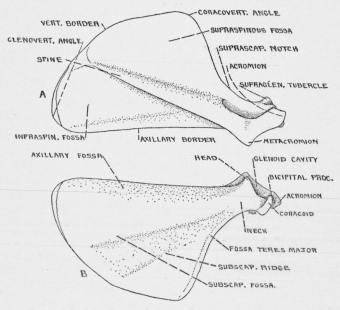

FIG. 30. Osteological details of the right scapula of *Teonoma*. *A*,
Lateral aspect. *B*, Medial aspect.

standing posture with the limb extended in a straight line.
In a plantigrade mammal this will be to the sole of the heel;
in a digitigrade one, to the tip of the toes, the hoof, or what-
ever portion of the foot rests upon the ground. In the genus
Neotoma the manus is relatively small and weak, and the
animal may be considered as really plantigrade in this
member (Plate 1 shows the fore foot as more digitigrade

than is actually the case). It will be seen, however, that in a skeleton this measurement can never be accurately taken, for the palmar pad is then always missing. In working on skeletons, therefore, it seems that the best way to arrive at the functional length of the fore limb is to consider this as consisting of the sum of the length of the humerus and the length of the radius. Unless accompanied by a phrase of qualification, this will always be considered as constituting the functional length of the fore limb when referring to *skeletal* characters in the present paper.

In any work concerning the comparative length of the limbs of mammals it is necessary to have another standard with which to compare the legs, and this can be neither the total length, nor the vertebral length, for the heads or tails of two dissimilar mammals may be short or long, respectively. The best measurement for comparison would therefore seem to be the body length, comprising the sum of the lengths of the cervical, thoracic, lumbar, and sacral vertebrae, and it should be understood that this is meant by body length when hereafter referring to skeletal matters.

Among the skeletons available there are eight of *Homodontomys*, only three of which are partially articulated, there are three *Neotoma*, all articulated; and there are four *Teonoma*, two being articulated. Practically none of these is perfect in every respect, and hence the series is not sufficiently large for the average to be dependable. The figures and slight differences should not, therefore, be considered as absolutely accurate; but the trends are undoubtedly trustworthy.

In the only three instances where this functional length of the fore leg could be calculated for *Homodontomys* it was found to average 44.4 (42.6 to 45.5) per cent of the body length; in three *Neotoma* 49.3 (48 to 51.6) per cent; and in two *Teonoma* 47.1 (46 to 48.1) per cent. The subgenus *Neotoma* thus exhibits a slight trend toward a longer fore leg which may or may not be real. It is somewhat at variance with expectations, for according to established beliefs, arboreal or other climbing habits should tend to lengthen the arm, and this subgenus is the least given to climbing of the three. It will be seen that an interpretation of this fact is difficult, for the apparent length of arm in *Neotoma* may signify merely that its body is somewhat shorter, or there may be conflicting trends which overbalance the influences of a more strictly terrestrial habitat.

Upper arm

Humerus. The humerus, which is the bone of the upper arm or brachium, articulates proximad with the scapula at the glenoid cavity, and distad with the radius and ulna. In *Homodontomys* it averaged 51.7 (50.7 to 52.8) per cent of the functional arm length; in *Neotoma*, 50.5 (50.4 to 50.8) per cent; and in *Teonoma*, 52.4 (51.7 to 52.7) per cent. There is no variation in this respect with age. The tendency is therefore for the animal which is least scansorial to have the shortest upper arm; but the difference is too slight to be of great importance.

The humerus is usually, but not always, slightly thicker and more massive in *Teonoma*, and perhaps least so in *Neotoma*. Most of the shaft, including the distal extremity, is straight, but the head, articulating with the scapula, is directed caudad, together with the small portion of the shaft immediately adjoining. The head is usually appreciably the largest in *Teonoma*. Cranio-laterad of the head is the greater tuberosity, upon which are inserted the supraspinatus, infraspinatus, teres minor, and a part of the pectoralis profundus anterior. From it originate portions of the triceps lateralis and the brachialis also. It must therefore reflect the influences of six different muscles, and any variation which may occur is correspondingly difficult to interpret. The only one of these muscles noted as showing

appreciable variation is the teres minor, slightly larger in
Neotoma and *Teonoma*. The shape of the greater tuberosity
is uniformly the same, being a trifle irregular and with a
slight depression upon the lateral portion. The tuberosity is,
however, somewhat smaller in *Neotoma*, and larger in
Teonoma, and in some specimens of both of these it extends
above the head, which it never does in *Homodontomys*.

The lesser tuberosity is but a third the size of the greater
and lies mediad to the head. The subscapularis is the only
muscle attached to it, and it varies more in size individually
than it does subgenerically; but is lighter in *Neotoma*. Between the lesser and greater tuberosities lies the bicipital
groove, over which passes the original portion of the biceps
brachii.

Extending distad from the lesser tuberosity is the medial
ridge, culminating at the first third of the humeral length
in a faint process, distad from which extends the usual
medial border of the shaft. Extending caudad from the
medial ridge, between the tuberosity and the process, is the
insertion of the pectoralis abdominalis. In *Teonoma* this
ridge is best developed, but this may be due more to mechanical than myological reasons. Upon the medial process
of the shaft, above described, are inserted the teres major
and latissimus dorsi, but the latter seems to occupy the most
prominent portion of the process, and the development of the
latter doubtless depends mostly upon this muscle. Its most
prominent development is certainly found in *Teonoma*, but
there is much individual variation in this respect and one
hesitates to make definite statements concerning it.

Extending distad from the greater tuberosity upon the
cranio-lateral border of the humerus is the deltoid ridge,
culminating in the spine of the same name. It is highly
developed in the present genus and the factors influencing
its size are complex. Along the medial border of the proximal
portion of the deltoid ridge are inserted the panniculus

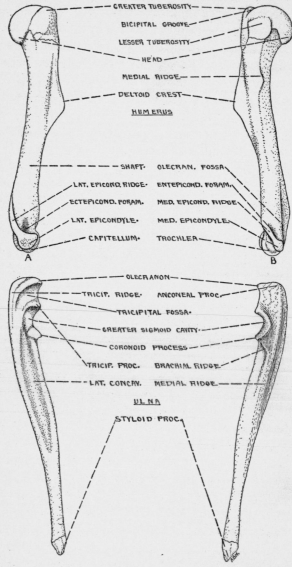

FIG. 31. Osteological details of the right humerus and ulna of *Teonoma*. *A*, Lateral aspect.   *B*, Medial aspect.

carnosus and pectoralis profundus anterior, the latter extending upon the greater tuberosity; along the same border of the distal ridge are inserted the pectorali superficialis and profundus posterior. Inserted chiefly upon the spine itself are the clavo-acromiodeltoid, and upon both the spine and the adjoining ridges the spinodeltoid and brachialis. There are thus seven muscles concerned with this feature of the humerus. The panniculus is the only one of these that is best developed in *Neotoma*, but the superficial pectoral is also more extensive than in *Homodontomys*, and in this animal the deltoid spine, but not the remainder of the deltoid ridge, is highest and most distinct. On the other hand, the pectorali superficialis and profundus posterior, and the clavo-acromiodeltoid seem to be best developed in *Teonoma*, and in this subgenus the deltoid spine as a whole is most extensive, although the spine is not as distinct as in *Neotoma*. The distance from the humeral head to the most prominent point of the spine is from 35 to 41 per cent of the length of this bone, the larger percentages usually occurring in *Teonoma*.

The origin of the triceps medialis extends from the process of the medial shaft along practically the entire olecranol fossa, but there is no variation in this part of the humerus. The same is to be said regarding the distal portion of the origin of the brachialis, distad from the deltoid ridge.

The distal termination of the humerus is characterized by the medial and lateral epicondyles. The greatest width of the distal portion of the humerus averages 23.8 per cent of its length in *Homodontomys*, 23.7 in *Neotoma* and 24.5 in *Teonoma*. The lateral epicondyle is the culmination of the very prominent epicondyloid ridge. This varies practically not at all subgenerically, but the individual difference is great. It may project a couple of millimeters laterad of the epicondyle or not at all. Origins of the extensores carpi radialis longus and brevis and digitorum communis are most intimately concerned with the epicondyloid ridge, while the origins of the extensores digiti quinti and carpi ulnaris belong more strictly to the lateral epicondyle proper. The latter is to all intents merely a continuation of the lateral articular eminence, although they have different centers of ossification. The chief eminence of the lateral portion of the surface of articulation is the capitellum, cranially situated, which articulates with the radius.

The more distal portion is a part of the trochlea, articulating with the ulna. Proximad of the capitellum is the ectepicondyloid foramen, always present save in the left humerus of a single specimen of *Teonoma*, in which the foramen is barely closed by a thin bony membrane. In others it varies somewhat in size.

The lateral epicondyle is situated a trifle nearer the humeral axis than is the medial, and much nearer the antibrachial axial center. The medial is considerably the more slender, and upon it originate eight muscles—the first and second heads of the flexor digitorum profundus, palmaris longus, flexores digitorum sublimis and carpi radialis, pronator teres, and anconeus. There is no appreciable variation of a subgeneric nature in the shape of this item, however, but there is some slight individual difference in its precise conformation.

Directly proximad of the trochlea is usually situated the entepicondyloid foramen, which is quite variable. In six *Homodontomys* it is present and in four absent, the skeletons being bilaterally symmetrical in this respect; in three *Neotoma* it is present; and in five *Teonoma* of the form *cinerea* it is present and in one of the form *occidentalis* it is absent. When absent it is not merely a case of a thin septum being present, but all signs of it are obliterated and the depressions upon either aspect of the bone are filled with bony tissue.

Forearm

The antibrachium consists of two bones, the ulna being the longer and the radius the shorter.

Ulna. In *Homodontomys* the ulna averages 58.3 (56.8 to 60) per cent of the functional arm length; in *Neotoma* it averages 60 (59.2 to 61) per cent; and in *Teonoma*, 57.9 (56.2 to 59) per cent. It is thus seen that in the animal which is presumably the poorest climber, the ulna, and therefore the forearm, averages appreciably longer with respect to body length than in the other two. As previously mentioned, this naturally accompanies a correspondingly short humerus.

The ulna, like most of the other bones, is least robust in *Neotoma*. Upon the cranial aspect near its proximal end is situated the greater sigmoid cavity, by which articulation with the humerus is effected. Upon the distal border of this occurs the coronoid process. Laterad upon the border of the latter there is a small facet for the articulation of the radius, and mediad the process is slightly extended, this marking the origination of the flexor digitorum sublimis. It is least accentuated in *Neotoma* and somewhat the best defined in *Teonoma*, as might be expected, for the muscle is larger in the latter animal and divides into four, instead of three tendons. Proximad of the sigmoid cavity occurs the olecranon, which plays an important part in the economy of the animal, for upon this extension of the forearm largely depends the leverage which that member can exert. Its extent proximad from the sigmoid cavity is from 11.3 to 13.3 per cent of the ulnar length. Laterad upon the proximal border of the sigmoid cavity is the tricipital process, perhaps a trifle the best defined in *Teonoma*. The triceps medialis is inserted upon this and the fossa immediately proximad, which is a bit the least distinct in *Homodontomys*. Caudad to this along the caudo-lateral border is the tricipital ridge, upon which is inserted the triceps lateralis, best developed of course, in old adults. Upon the posterior or proximal aspect of the olecranon is inserted the triceps longus, and directly distad upon the slightly defined anconeal process on the medial side is the insertion of the anconeus, in definition variable with age. Along the caudo-medial border distad from the olecranon for one-third the length of the ulna the flexor carpi ulnaris takes partial origin, but only the proximal portion of this is indicated by a slight ridge. Similarly situated upon the central half of the shaft is the ulnar portion of the origin of the third head of the flexor digitorum profundus. Upon the distal third of the medial border of the shaft is a slight ridge, from which the pronator quadratus takes origin. Just distad of the coronoid process upon the medial border is located the short brachial ridge, upon which is inserted the brachialis. If anything it is best defined in *Teonoma*, although no difference was noted in this muscle during dissection. Upon the lateral aspect of the ulna is found the lateral concavity or fossa. Upon the caudal border of this originates the extensor indicis, and from the cranial border, the ulnar portion of the extensor metacarpi pollicis.

The distal termination of the ulna consists of the conical styloid process, the caudo-lateral aspect of which is grooved for the passage of tendons. Articulation is with the triquetrum.

Radius. In *Homodontomys* the radius averages 83.2 (81.8 to 85.3) per cent of the ulnar length; in *Neotoma* the average is 82.3 (81.5 to 82.8); and in *Teonoma* 82.5 (80.6 to 84.5) per cent.

All except the distal portion of the radius is situated fairly upon the cranial aspect of the forearm. It consists of a shaft with an enlarged extremity at either end, the distal one being much the larger. Upon its proximal extremity there is a facet for articulation with the capitellum of the humerus, but there is no appreciably defined articular circumference at the point of junction of this head with the ulna. There is much variation in the diameter of the shaft but the tendency is for this to be smallest in *Neotoma*—especially the distal portion—and largest in *Teonoma*. Upon the mediocaudal border of the shaft near the head is the slight tuberosity, equally well marked in the three subgenera, upon which is inserted the biceps. The cranial ridge, upon the medial side of which is inserted the pronator teres, and upon the lateral, the supinator, is readily distinguishable in some animals, but in others considerably older it may be practically undefined. Other muscles attached to this bone are the extensor metacarpi pollicis and pronator quadratus. Their positions upon the shaft are barely traceable by faint ridges, in the development of which there is little or no variation. The caudal border of the distal portion of the shaft bears a flat facet for articulation with the ulna. The distal termination is very irregular in precise shape, but the only feature of especial application are the pointed, terminal, styloid process, and the concave facet for articulation with the scapholunar bone.

Hand

The distal extremity of the radius is considerably larger than that of the ulna. In relaxed position the lateral border of the latter lies a shade laterad to that of the former, when the shaft of the humerus is vertical. This, however, throws the medial border of the distal extremity of the radius considerably mediad to that of the ulna. The palm of the hand is therefore inclined with the thumb inward at ten to fifteen degrees from vertical. Supination is possible only to 90 degrees, while pronation can throw the palm to but slightly beyond the horizontal, thus making the possible movement of this member about 100 degrees, instead of some 180 as is usual in man.

In most of the skeletons the fore foot was disarticulated, and of those in which it could be measured, the digits were flexed in varying degree so that the entire length of the hand could be calculated only approximately. Tentatively, then, the entire fore foot, including the digits and claws, is about 24 to 25 per cent of the arm length in *Homodontomys;* 26 to 28 in *Neotoma;* and 28 to 31 per cent in *Teonoma.*

Carpus. The bones of the carpus number 9, as follows: Beginning at the lateral side, the first bone is the triquetrum, articulating with the ulna. Articulating with the triquetrum upon its palmar face is the pisiform bone, of characteristic shape, with a palmar, spherical process. Upon the latter is inserted the flexor carpi ulnaris, and from it originates the abductor digiti quinti.[1] To it is also attached, as an anchor, the tough tissue about the extremity of the falciform. Next mediad to the triquetrum is the larger scapholunar bone, articulating with the radius. Next, upon the medial border of the carpus may be the falciform, which is usually lost during the cleaning of the bones, with attachment to the scapholunar. From the vicinity of its base originates the abductor pollicis brevis. In *Homodontomys* and *Neotoma* it may be more proper to consider this as two bones—a sesamoid articulating loosely with the scapholunar, with a slender falciform bone extending over the palm, imbedded in and lending substance to the cartilaginous tissue of the palm and attached by the same to the pisiform. Beneath it pass most of the tendons of the palm. In *Teonoma* the falciform is absent.

In the second series of carpal bones, from the lateral side, are the hamatum, which is relatively large, and adjoins the strongly triangular capitatum. The smaller centrale comes next, followed respectively by the multangula minus and majus, the latter lying laterad to metacarpus one.

[1] The attachments of the smaller muscles of the hand proper are not shown in the osteological illustrations.

Metacarpus. The metacarpals number five. The first, belonging to the pollex, is very short but extends, with the second metacarpal, farther proximad than any of the others. The head of the latter has a medial fossa for articulation with the multangulum minus. The proximal terminations of the third and fourth are situated consecutively farther distad, as is the medial portion of the fifth, but of the last there is a lateral extension proximad for articulation with the hamatum. The longest of the metacarpals is the third. Taking this as representing 100, we get the following values from the others. In *Homodontomys* the first is 41; the second 82; the fourth 92; and the fifth 75. In *Neotoma* the first is 27; the second 83; the fourth 92; and the fifth 73. In *Teonoma* the first is 43; the second 84; the fourth 93; and the fifth 75. There is thus very slight variation in the relative length of the metacarpals, save that the pollex is the most rudimentary in the least scansorial subgenus.

The flexor carpi radialis is inserted upon the palmar aspect of the base of metacarpal two. Upon the dorsal surface of the manus, the extensor metacarpi pollicis has insertion upon metacarpus one, the extensores carpi radialis longus and brevis respectively on the second and third, and the extensor carpi ulnaris upon the fifth.

Digits. There are two phalanges upon the pollex or first digit, although the terminal one is but a minute nubbin, without a nail. There are three phalanges to each of the remaining four digits, although the terminal ones, from which extend the claws, are so small and surrounded in the usual cleaned specimen by dry cartilaginous tissue that it is difficult to define them.

Due to the extreme tenuousness of many of the digital tendons and the great difficulty experienced in separating them from their connective tissue, it is impossible to be certain regarding the exact point of insertion upon the phalanges of some of them. This has been illustrated as exactly as possible, however, in the accompanying figures.

Upon digit one are inserted tendons of the extensor indicis and the third head of the flexor digitorum profundus. Upon digit two are a tendon of the extensor digitorum communis, extensor indicis, flexor digitorum sublimis, and tendons from two heads of the flexor digitorum profundus. On digit three are inserted two tendons from the extensor digitorum communis, one from the flexor digitorum sublimis, and two heads of the flexor digitorum profundus. Digit four has tendons from the extensores digiti quinti and digitorum communis, and from the flexores digitorum sublimis and the third head of the digitorum profundus. On digit five are the extensores digiti quinti and digitorum communis, and third head of the flexor profundus. In *Teonoma* the extensor digitorum communis and flexor digitorum sublimis muscles, with their distal tendons, are appreciably more robust, and in addition, the latter muscle sends a fifth tendon to digit five. The lateral side of the manus in this subgenus is strengthened to just this extent.

Pelvic girdle

As with the pectoral girdle, the affinity of the pelvic girdle is supposed to be with the vertebral column rather than with the limbs; but the functions of the muscles attached to it make it far more convenient to discuss this girdle in connection with the neighboring appendages.

The pectoral girdle is formed by the two innominate bones, the greatest length of which varies from about 32 to 35 per cent of the vertebral body length. There is almost no subgeneric variation in this respect. Each innominate consists of four bones, as figured. The ilium is the one most craniad, extending to the acetabulum; the cotyloid bone comprises most of the acetabulum and articulates with the three other bones, but does not extend to the medial surface of the innominate; the ischium forms the caudo-dorsal portion of the innominate, articulating at the symphysis with the pubis, which then passes craniad to the acetabulum. The pubo-ischial articulation is not shown by any specimen at hand, and its precise position is inferred; but the other articulations of the four bones are clearly traceable in skeletons of two young individuals, although they are entirely obliterated in those that are fully adult.

There are thirty muscle and tendon attachments upon the innominate, and it is impossible, therefore, to interpret the effects which many of them have had upon the bony framework. The length of the pelvis varies from 44 to 48 per cent of the functional length of the hind leg, and there is no sub-generic variation in this respect. The length of the ilium, measured from the cranial border of the acetabulum, is from 57 to 61.6 per cent of the length of the innominate, and the ischial depth, from 32.9 to 38.1 per cent of the same. These measurements, even the last, exhibit surprisingly little individual variation, but the differences in the precise configuration of the details are great, and in fact hardly any two innominates are exactly alike. This is especially noticeable in the shape of the pelvic arch, which varies individually in both sexes from V-shaped to U-shaped. So far as known the pelvic arch is always closed by the symphysis pubis in the present genus. The differences shown in the degree of divergence of the cranial portion of the ilia are also well nigh infinite, as is the precise position of the articulation with the sacrum, as previously noted. Thus the terminations of the transverse processes of the sixth lumbar vertebra may be situated slightly craniad or considerably caudad to the cranial ends of the ilia. The arc of the lateral ridge extending from the spine may have a relatively slight or a sharp curve, the latter circumstance causing the spine to project sharply laterad. These variations seem to be purely individual.

Attention should again be called to the fact that especially in the case of the innominate, many of the muscle attachments are aponeurotic and exceedingly thin, so that a number may occupy a very narrow space. In making them sufficiently wide in the illustrations for proper definition, distortion in respect to their precise locations upon the bones has been inevitable.

The cranio-lateral process of the ilium is termed the spine, and from it originates Poupart's ligament. The craniomedial face of this may project farther craniad than the spine itself, and from this portion originates part of the longissimus dorsi. As previously mentioned, there is much individual variation at this point. From the spine extend two borders and a ridge. The superior border exhibits variation, chiefly due to the fact that a good portion of it articulates, upon its medial surface, with the sacrum; but from its caudal portion originates the gemellus superior. At a point about three-fifths caudad along the superior border is the posterior superior spine, marking the caudal termination of the articulation with the sacrum. Just caudad of this is situated the gluteal notch, over which passes the superior gluteal nerve. Upon the lateral ridge there is no muscle attached, but between this and the superior border lies the superior gluteal fossa, giving origin to the gluteus medius, and between it and the inferior border is the inferior gluteal fossa, from which originates the gluteus minimus. Adjoining the latter upon the cranial portion of the inferior border is the origin of the gluteus superficialis anterior, and mediad, that of the iliacus, which follows the well-defined iliacal ridge almost to the femoral process. There is great variation in all of these details, but this seems to be purely individual. Immediately craniad of the acetabulum is the femoral process, from which originates the rectus femoris.

Upon the medial side of the ilium is located the extensive and variable articular surface, by which the innominate is joined to the sacrum. Upon the cranio-ventral border is usually, though not always, a small process upon which is inserted a portion of the quadratus lumborum. Upon the ventral border caudad to the articular surface is inserted the abductor caudae internus, and upon the medial aspect of the pectineal process, ventrad of the acetabulum, is inserted the psoas minor.

The acetabulum, or cotyloid articular cavity, lies at the junction of the four bones of the innominate. Upon the caudo-ventral border of its rim is situated the cotyloid notch, through which pass the blood vessels and nerves of the hip joint. It may be bridged either by a ligament or by bone. The cranial and ventral borders of the acetabulum are formed by the cotyloid bone, but the caudal border of this is within the cavity and it does not extend to the medial surface of the innominate. It articulates with the three other bones of the innominate, and as previously mentioned, sutures are discernible only in immature animals.

The ischium comprises the caudo-dorsal portion of the innominate, extending from the acetabulum to (presumably) approximately the center of the symphysis. A notable variation is in the caudal border of the ascending ramus, which may incline at such angle that the superior tuberosity may be situated either considerably craniad or considerably caudad of the inferior tuberosity of the ischium. In all other points there is also variation of the ischium, but not to so notable a degree; and there are so many muscles attached to this bone that it is impossible to interpret the differences with any confidence.

Immediately caudad of the acetabulum upon the dorsal border is the sciatic notch, and adjoining it, the gemellus fossa, from which originates the gemellus inferior. In some specimens it is well marked, but in others its definition is poor. The dorso-caudal angle of the ischium, or superior tuberosity, shows great variation in its precise conformation, but from it originate the semimembranosus anticus when this is present, the second or ischial head of the semitendinosus, the biceps femoris posticus, and a part of the semi-membranosus posticus. It is thus well nigh impossible to unravel the myological stimuli operating upon the bone. The presence or absence of the semimembranosus anticus is individually variable, and to this may be attributable a part of the osteological differences encountered. Upon the caudal border of the ascending ramus of the pubis originate the ischiocavernosus, gracilis posticus, and the more ventral portion of the origin of the semimembranosus posticus. Differences in the pull of these muscles are undoubtedly accountable for the fact that the caudal border of the ramus may be straight, or the ventral portion definitely indented.

Over most of the lateral face of the ischium originates the quadratus femoris, and along the obturator border of both this bone and the pubis originates the obturator externus. Upon the inferior tuberosity of the ischium arises Poupart's ligament, and closely adjoining, parts of the gracilis posticus, rectus abdominis, and adductor brevis. The variation in its shape is great, but this is individual. The only muscle arising upon the medial face of the ischium is the obturator internus from the extensive fossa of the same name.

The pubis articulates caudad with the ischium at the symphysis, and craniad near the acetabulum with the coty-loid and ischium. It, with the ischium, encloses the obtur-ator foramen. This bone shows but little variation save in length, the latter item being influenced not directly by muscular attachments but rather in accordance with differ-ences in the ascending ramus and the position of the inferior tuberosity of the ischium.

From the pubis originate a portion of the rectus ab-dominis, adductor longus, gracilis anticus, the anterior por-tion of the adductor brevis, obturator externus, and the adductor magnus. The latter arises chiefly from a point ventrad the acetabulum. The pectineus has origin from the pectineal process upon the ventral border also ventrad of the acetabulum. This process, however, is undeveloped in animals sufficiently young for the sutures of the innominate to show, and it is not known with certainty whether it more properly belongs with the pubis or ilium. Upon the caudal border of the medial surface of the pubis originates the abductor caudae externus.

Thus, although there is much variation shown by certain parts of the innominate, these are individual, and there is no single group character. In addition, there are comparatively few details which are amenable to the influences of but a single muscle.

Posterior limb

The true length of the hind limb in a plantigrade mammal is the sum of the length of the femur and the distance from the knee joint to the ground upon which it stands. In a digitigrade type the latter item is also the distance to the ground or to the tip of the toes or hoof. The genus *Neotoma* is neither plantigrade nor digitigrade. When at rest the entire foot is placed upon the ground, but when running, it, like most rodents, raises the heel smartly. The functional limb length must, therefore, be considered as terminating at some point between the heel and the toe, and it is obviously necessary that some arbitrary point be assigned for this; which we can only hope represents the true condition to an approximate extent. In running, the digits may be presumed to play a rather slight part, the "ball" of the foot, at the tarsal terminations, giving the final impetus to the stride. In such an animal, therefore, that is neither plantigrade nor digitigrade, it seems logical to consider that half the distance from the heel to the end of the longest metatarsal bone constitutes the termination of the length of the hind limb from a functional, as opposed to an anatomical, viewpoint. This, it should be mentioned again, is open to the serious objection that it is arbitrary and inaccurate to

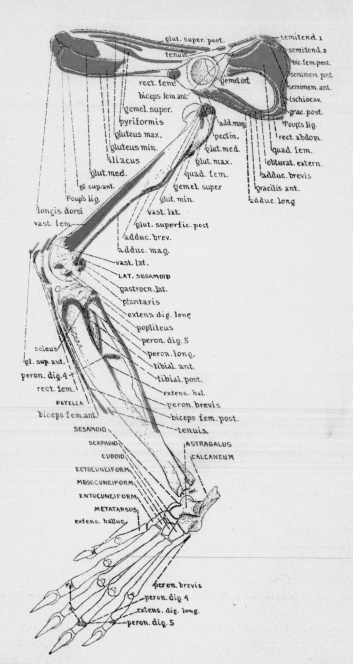

FIG. 32. Lateral aspect of left innominate and hind limb of *Teonoma*, showing muscle attachments (origins in blue, insertions in red). Foot rotated to show dorsum.

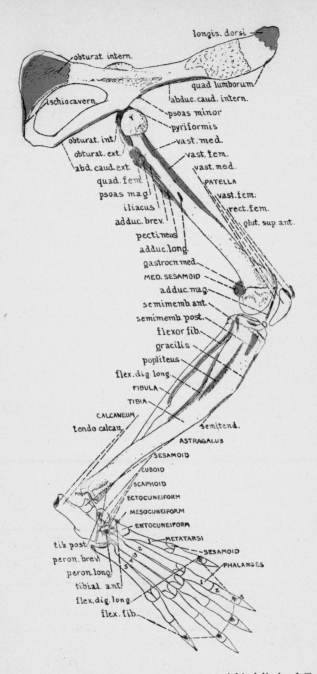

Fig. 33. Medial aspect of left innominate and hind limb of *Teonoma*, showing muscle attachments. Foot rotated to show plantar aspect.

161

an unknown extent, but some such standard must be taken in the present work. When mentioned hereafter, the term functional length of leg, therefore, comprises the sum of lengths of femur, of the tibia, and half the distance from the heel to the end of the longest metatarsal. Unfortunately, but two of the skeletons of *Homodontomys*, three of *Neotoma* and two of *Teonoma*, were accompanied by articulated feet, so that this detail could be calculated for but this number.

The functional length of the hind leg, as calculated by the above formula, varies from 64.7 to 68.2 per cent of the length of the body vertebrae in *Homodontomys*; from 74 to 78 in *Neotoma;* and from 72 to 75 per cent in *Teonoma*. In *Homodontomys* it is from 31.7 to 34 per cent longer than the functional length of the fore limb; in *Neotoma*, from 33.4 to 34.8 per cent, and in *Teonoma*, 36 per cent.

Thigh

Femur. The femur or thigh bone has a length in *Homodontomys* of from 41.7 to 42.4 per cent of the functional length of the leg; in *Neotoma* from 41.7 to 42.3 per cent; and in *Teonoma*, 43.2 per cent. (In *N. f. rubida* the average is 40.8 per cent.)

Upon the medial side of the proximal end of the femur is situated the circular head, articulating with the acetabulum. It is connected with the shaft by a constricted neck, and has a depression upon the medial aspect of its circumference for the reception of the ligamentum teres. The great trochanter is located laterad to the head and is a continuation of, and in direct line with, the shaft. It projects from one to two millimeters proximad of the head. Upon its lateral surface is inserted the gluteus minimus, gemellus superior, and gluteus medius, and upon its caudal border, termed the intertrochanteric line, a portion of the gluteus maximus. Upon its cranial portion, constituting the proximal termination of the lateral ridge of the femur, originate the vastus

lateralis and a portion of the vastus femoris. The trochanteric notch joins the border of the great trochanter
to the head, and upon the medial aspect of the trochanter
itself is the trochanteric fossa, relatively very deep, into
which are inserted both obturator muscles, and upon its
proximal border, the pyriformis. There is practically no
osteological variation.

Disto-caudad to the head upon the medial portion of the
shaft projects the lesser trochanter. Upon the caudal aspect
of this is inserted the quadratus femoris, and craniad, a part
of the pectineus, the psoas magnus and the iliacus. The

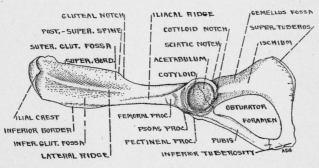

FIG. 34. Lateral aspect of left innominate of *Teonoma*, showing osteological details.

lesser trochanter is a trifle the best developed in *Teonoma*,
but during dissection no subgeneric differences were noted
in the muscles concerned. The insertion of the pectineus
extends distad to almost the center of the shaft, but this is
not indicated osteologically. Medio-caudad upon the
shaft, variably at about its center, is sometimes, but not
usually, a small roughened area that marks the insertion
of the adductor longus. Distad from the head upon the
medial shaft is the origin of the vastus medialis, and just
craniad, for practically the entire length of the shaft upon
its cranial border, that of the vastus femoris; but there is no
osteological indication of either.

Distad of the great trochanter the lateral ridge rises to form the lateral crest, or third trochanter of the femur. The cranial surface of this is slightly concave, to an individually differing degree, and as might be expected, the crest is relatively less developed in young animals. There is much individual, but practically no subgeneric variation. Upon both borders of the crest proper and for some distance upon either ridge adjoining is inserted the adductor brevis, and immediately caudad, the gluteus superficialis posterior. Distad, in line with the crest for half the length of the shaft, is inserted the adductor magnus.

The femur ends distad in two condyles separated craniad by the trochlea for the reception of the patella, and caudad by the intercondyloid fossa. Upon the lateral epicondyle there may usually be descried three slight fossa—the disto-caudal one for the origin of the popliteus; the disto-cranial for the insertion of the extensor digitorum longus; and the more proximal for the attachment of the external collateral ligament. A corresponding fossa upon the medial epicondyle is for the attachment of the internal collateral ligament. There is a caudal angle to each condyle, within which is situated the lateral and medial sesamoid bones respectively. They are really invested in the heads of the gastrocnemii lateralis and medialis. In addition there are two smaller, anterior sesamoids, invested in the semilunar cartilages of the knee joint and situated one at the ental margin of either condyle, between the femur and tibia.

The only remaining muscle having attachment upon the femur is the plantaris, which arises from the tissue adjoining the lateral sesamoid, and to a slight extent from the lateral epicondyle itself.

Lower leg

Patella. Although a distinct bone, the patella or knee cap is analogous to the olecranon of the fore limb. It is about 13

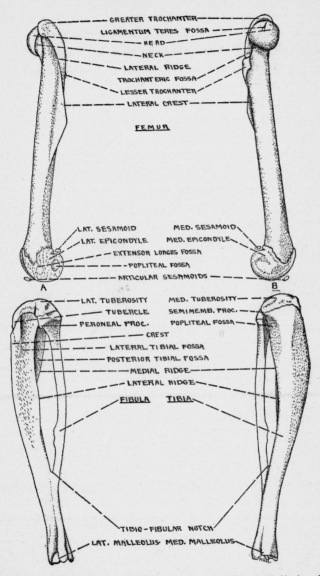

GREATER TROCHANTER
LIGAMENTUM TERES FOSSA
HEAD
NECK
LATERAL RIDGE
TROCHANTERIC FOSSA
LESSER TROCHANTER
LATERAL CREST

FEMUR

LAT. SESAMOID   MED. SESAMOID
LAT. EPICONDYLE   MED. EPICONDYLE
EXTENSOR LONGUS FOSSA
POPLITEAL FOSSA
ARTICULAR SESAMOIDS

A   B

LAT. TUBEROSITY   MED. TUBEROSITY
TUBERCLE   SEMIMEMB. PROC.
PERONEAL PROC.   POPLITEAL FOSSA
CREST
LATERAL TIBIAL FOSSA
POSTERIOR TIBIAL FOSSA
MEDIAL RIDGE
LATERAL RIDGE

FIBULA   TIBIA

TIBIO-FIBULAR NOTCH
LAT. MALLEOLUS MED. MALLEOLUS

Fig. 35. Osteological details of the left femur, tibia and fibula of *Teonoma*. *A*, Lateral aspect. *B*, Medial aspect.

or 14 per cent of the length of the tibia, is usually described as pear-shaped (although like half a pear would be more appropriate), and fits against the trochlea of the femur. It is imbedded in the capsule of the joint, and the patella ligament passes from its distal end to the tibia.

Upon the cranio-proximal part of the patella is inserted the rectus femoris, and on the latero-distal part, the biceps femoris anticus. Upon the tendinous tissue cranio-proximad and mediad to the patella are inserted the gluteus superficialis anterior, vasti lateralis, medialis, and femoris, and the adductor magnus.

Tibia. The tibia is the longer of the two bones of the lower leg, and is seldom shorter than the femur. In *Homodontomys* it measures from 44.7 to 45.2 per cent of the functional length of the hind leg; in *Neotoma*, from 44.3 to 44.8 per cent; and in *Teonoma* a trifle less—about 43 per cent. It is relatively lightest in *Neotoma*, and considerably the most robust in *Teonoma*.

The proximal head of the tibia is divided into a lateral and a medial tuberosity, with a slight depression between. Distad to the head, upon the cranial border, is the tubercle. This has its own center of ossification, and the distal margin is often separated from the shaft in the case of a well-cleaned skeleton. The lateral tuberosity has a caudal projection with an articular surface for the attachment of the fibula.

The cranio-medial border of the shaft is largely devoid of muscle. Upon the extreme cranio-medial portion adjoining the head is inserted the semimembranosus anticus. This point is marked by a roughness which stands in relief from the remainder of the shaft—not a true process, as it conforms to the shape of the head, but one to all intents. It is considerably best defined in *Teonoma*, although in that animal the attached muscle appears no larger. Distad of the above prominence is situated the popliteal fossa, over which passes the popliteus. It is best defined in *Teonoma* for the reason of the greater prominence of the bone at the insertion of the semimembranosus anticus in that subgenus. The actual insertion of the popliteus is along a slight ridge, definable only in fully adult specimens, that occurs over this portion of the shaft near its center. Immediately laterad, near the proximal end, is the unmarked insertion of the semimembranosus posticus. Upon the proximal portion of the crest of the tibia, or cranio-lateral border, is inserted the gracilis, and farther distad, the semitendinosus. From the medial ridge arises the flexor digitorum longus.

Upon the superficial fascia upon the cranio-lateral portion of the lower leg for half the length of the tibia is inserted the biceps femoris posticus, and immediately distad, the tenuissimus. The lateral tibial fossa is located upon the lateral aspect of the bone. It is shallowest in *Neotoma* and slightly deepest in *Teonoma*. From its proximal border and adjoining portion of the caudal border arises the tibialis anticus. Farther distad the extensor hallucis arises upon the fascia extending from this border.

The posterior tibial fossa is situated upon the caudal aspect of the bone. From a portion of the medial border of this, along a well-defined crest, arises the tibialis posticus.

Upon the caudo-lateral portion of the distal shaft is the articular surface with which the fibia is fused, as described for the latter bone.

The distal end of the tibia has three articular processes, for articulation with the foot. The medial surface of two of these constitutes the internal malleolus, with a well-defined groove for the passage of tendons, least well marked in *Neotoma* and best in *Teonoma*. In common with the remainder of the bone the distal extremity is somewhat the lightest in the former and most robust in the latter subgenus.

Fibula. The fibula, is situated slightly latero-caudad of the tibia. It is but a trifle shorter than the latter bone, but the distance to the point at which the two fuse varies in *Homodontomys* from 54.6 to 60 per cent the length of the tibia; in *Neotoma*, from 62.3 to 64.2; and in *Teonoma* from 56 to 60.7 per cent.

The head of the fibula, which is much the largest in *Teonoma*, articulates with a process upon the caudal portion of the lateral tuberosity of the tibia. The lateral part of the head forms a well-marked process for the origin of the peroneus longus. Just mediad is a very faint process for the origin of the peroneus digiti quinti, definable only in very old individuals. With the latter may arise the peroneus digiti quarti, or it may have origin from the ectal belly of the peroneus quinti. The peroneus brevis takes origin from the medial portion of the head along the medial border of the shaft of the fibula. Upon the cranio-medial border, as well as the adjoining part of the medial tuberosity, originates the flexor fibularis, which may be responsible for a variably roughened area situated craniad upon the distal shaft.

At a point distad about two-thirds the length of the fibula the latter joins the tibia, forming at this point the tibio-fibular notch, and for some distance the two bones are firmly ankylosed; but they may separate in the case of specimens that have been cooked too long in cleaning. This portion of the fibula appears as no more than a well-defined ridge upon the shaft of the tibia, but the distal portion of the fibula is really free from its neighbor for several millimeters, or at least very lightly attached. The distal termination of the fibula broadens, and constitutes the external malleolus.

Foot

In man, supination of the foot is possible through about 60 degrees; pronation, on the average, probably not more than 10; and rotation, without the aid of other movement of this member, through something less than 90 degrees. Certain individuals can surpass these figures, however, and it is probable that many other mammals, fitted for a special sort of agility, are considerably more gifted in these respects. Because of the rigid ankylosis of the tibia and fibula of the genus *Neotoma* into a single osteological unit, appreciable rotation of the foot at the ankle joint is impossible. Partly due to the great mobility of the long metatarsus, supination of the anterior plantar surface, though of course not the heel, may be as far as 100 degrees, and what is more surprising, pronatino to 75 degrees from the horizontal is permitted. The reason for this is partly the form of the articular surfaces of the ankle, but there are other reasons as well, not so easy of investigation, as elsewhere discussed. When rotation of the foot is desired, this end is gained by a rotation of the whole leg at the hip.

Due to the flexion of the toes, the length of the foot is extremely difficult to obtain with exactitude from a skeleton, and one can but compute it with as much accuracy as possible. In *Homodontomys* the length of the entire foot constitutes from 37 to 38 per cent of the functional length of the hind leg; in *Neotoma*, from 38.8 to 40.8; and in *Teonoma* it is from 39.6 to 41.4 per cent. (In a single specimen of *Neotoma p. pennsylvanica*, an animal which seems invariably to live in the crevices of rocky cliffs, this percentage rises to 46.5, and in the small *Neotoma lepida stephensi*, it is but 35.2.)

Tarsus. The tarsus is composed of eight bones. The bone of the ankle joint, upon the dorsum, is the astragalus, articulating dorsad with the tibia and fibula. Its chief details are the articular surface, the neck, and the head extending distad. It also articulates with the calcaneum, scaphoid and tarsal sesamoid bones. To it are attached the quadratus plantae, abductor digiti quinti, and flexor digiti quinti brevis.

The proximal tarsal bone upon the plantar aspect is the calcaneum, the most massive bone of the foot. Its chief interest to the present contribution lies in its greater or caudal process, extending caudad from the heel, for it is upon the slightly concave termination of this that the tendo Achillis is inserted, and so it plays the rôle of lever, operated by the great extensors of the foot, and functionally, it is one of the most important osteological features of the leg. The length of this process, measured from the proximal termination of the astragalus, is individually quite variable, which can not be correlated with any other feature. Dorsad there are two facets, separated by a groove, for the articulation of the astragalus. The lower or medial facet is borne upon the sustentaculum, also termed the lesser process, but this name is untenable in the present instance, and had preferably be called the medial process. It is well formed, and deeply grooved upon the plantar aspect for the passage of flexor tendons. The more lateral, or tibial facet, is much more prominent and constitutes a well-defined crest upon the bone. Upon the lateral border of the bone is the shelf-like peroneal process, grooved upon the plantar aspect of its border for the passage of the peroneus longus tendon. Distad there is a facet for articulation with the cuboid, while disto-mediad there is articulation with the tarsal sesamoid. The only leg muscles having insertion upon the calcaneum are those connected with the tendo calcaneus, but the quadratus plantae, abductor digiti quinti, and flexor digiti quinti brevis have direct connection with this bone, while the extensor digitorum brevis has origin from the calcaneal ligament.

The tarsal sesamoid is small, flat, and almost circular in outline. It is situated upon the medial tarsus and articulates chiefly with the astragalus and calcaneum, and to a lesser extent with the entocuneiform and scaphoid. Upon it is inserted the tibialis posticus.

The cuboid is the bone immediately distad to the calcaneum and is the most lateral one of the distal series of tarsal bones. It is deeply grooved upon its plantar surface for the passage of the peroneus longus. In addition to the calcaneum, it articulates with the scaphoid, ectocuneiform and the fourth and fifth metatarsals.

Immediately distad of the astragalus is the scaphoid, considerably broader dorsad than ventrad. This articulates with all the bones of the tarsus save the calcaneum, and from it the abductor hallucis originates. It is as broad as both the ecto- and mesocuneiforms together.

The ectocuneiform is the connecting link between the scaphoid and third metatarsal, and is of the same width as the latter. Upon its plantar surface is inserted the tendon of the peroneus longus, and from it originate one head of the flexor hallucis brevis and the adductor digiti secundi.

The mesocuneiform is smaller than the last, but occupies an analogous position between the scaphoid and the second metatarsal.

The entocuneiform is the most medial one of the cuneiforms and the longest, lying mediad to the scaphoid, mesocuneiform and a portion of metatarsal one. It also articulates with the tarsal sesamoid bone. Upon it is inserted the tendon of the tibialis anticus, and from it arise one head of the flexor hallucis brevis and adductor digiti quarti.

Metatarsus. The first metatarsal is much the shortest, and about two-thirds as broad as the widest, which is the second. The fifth extends far proximad to laterad and ventrad of the tarsus, in the form of the peroneal process, upon which is inserted the peroneus brevis. Measuring the visible length of each metatarsal along its dorsum, and taking the length of the longest, which is the fifth, as representing 100, we get the following approximate values for the four others. In *Homodontomys* the first is 53; the second and third 88; and the fourth 94. In *Neotoma* the first is 54; the second 91; the third 94; and the fourth 93. In *Teonoma* the first is 57; the second 87; the third 96; and the fourth 95. There is, of course, some individual variation in this respect.

There is a pair of metatarso-phalangeal sesamoid bones to each digit, at the joint and in the position indicated in the illustrations.

There are two phalanges in the first digit and three in each of the other four. Of the latter, the proximal phalanges are longer than the second, while the terminal phalanx of each digit is minute, serving as a support for the claw. They can not be examined without disarticulation and careful cleaning.

As previously mentioned, the distal extremities of some of the tendons are so tenuous that the precise points at which they are inserted upon the digits are in doubt. Upon digit one are inserted tendons of the flexor digitorum longus, flexor fibularis, and extensor hallucis. Upon digits two and three, the extensores digitorum brevis and longus, plantaris, and flexor fibularis. On digit four, the plantaris, flexor fibularis, extensor digitorum longus, and peroneus digiti quarti. The same are attached to digit five, except that the peroneus digiti quinti takes the place of the peroneus quarti. The only appreciable subgeneric differences shown are that in *Teonoma* a branch of the plantaris extends also to digit one, and the peroneus digiti quarti sends two branches, instead of one, to digit four. This difference is probably not sufficient to prove of much functional importance to the animal.

CHAPTER IX

DISCUSSION

DISCUSSION OF MUSCLE ACTION AND LIMB MOTION

Investigation of the functions of muscles and analysis of their actions is so beset with difficulties that it is impossible to do a great deal in this line with the lower mammals by existing technique. Even in man, an investigation of the actions of the deeper muscles is anything but easy, and much more difficult in the case of other mammals. We know what a muscle *can* do perhaps, by noting the positions of origin and insertion, and further information may be obtained by observations of action and by stimulating a nerve electrically. But the important point is to know the part that it plays in action of muscle groups, and this can rarely be ascertained.

When we give thought to the matter it is seen that even such a simple act as scratching one's ear is, in reality, exceedingly involved. Then too, the same act may be simple or complex. Thus, the opening of a drawer may necessitate merely the flexion of a finger and then of the arm, or if the drawer sticks, it may be necessary to bring into play most of the muscles of the body. One must consider that the precise method by which an action is controlled is unknown. We may stretch forth an arm merely to touch the most fragile object or to fell an enemy. We may know that a muscle is an extensor of a certain part, but we do not know under just what conditions it may or may not act as such.

It is beyond the province of the present paper to present in detail what is known of muscle structure and the physiological manner in which action is accomplished. Certain

173

basic principles must be mentioned, however, in order that a logical discussion may be presented.

Each muscle is composed of a varying number of fibers. The longer the fibers, the greater is the possible distance of contraction. The more numerous the fibers the stronger the muscle is supposed to be. Thus, a pennated muscle is more powerful than a longitudinal one. Each muscle fiber has its own, separate, nerve fiber and motor ending, by which its orders are received. It is a matter of controversy whether, during gentle movements, each fiber of the muscle involved contracts but a fraction of the distance of which it is capable, or whether a small proportion of the fibers contract strongly while the remainder rest inactive—in other words, that selective action of the fibers is involved. Personally the writer favors the former hypothesis.

Possible movement of a muscle depends upon the condition both of the muscle fibers and of their nerve fibers and endings. Probably upon both of the foregoing depends the tone, or normal tension of a muscle. When the tone is poor, a muscle is flabby and soft; when it is good, the muscle is hard and springy. Exercise improves the texture of the muscle fibers and also enlarges and makes more sensitive the motor endings of the nerve fibers concerned. The precise conditions involved are unknown, but a muscle may gain in strength without a corresponding gain in quickness, and similarly, quickness and expertness in the action of a muscle may be increased without appreciably adding to its strength. The truly marvelous adroitness in manual movements exhibited by an expert in legerdemain is a result of hypersensitiveness and responsiveness of the nerve endings of the hand muscles, rather than of the muscles themselves—to such an extent that the majority of the movements involved have become in reality reflex, extraordinarily swift, and complex to a surprising degree.

In actual practice a small man of slight physique is often

more efficient in muscular action than a larger, who may be to all intents in equally good physical condition. We designate the smaller as "wiry," but in reality the nerve fibers governing the actions of his muscles are probably more sensitive and efficiently responsive to stimuli. Again, one man may have a reserve of so-called nervous energy which another lacks. In athletic competition the writer has attained results of which he was incapable without the nervous stimulus which such competition induced. Finally, he has personally known a man who was subject to epileptic fits to exhibit during such a seizure a phenomenal amount of strength that must have been close to one hundred per cent greater than that of which he was usually capable; and a man may also perform very unusual feats of strength while hypnotized.

The above facts indicate that the quality of muscular action is directly dependent, to a greater degree than is popularly realized, upon the quality of nervous impulse which the muscles receive, and this may be designated as nervous tone, as contrasted with muscular tone. Its average is fairly constant for a given group—genus or subfamily—but there is no reason for presuming that the nervous tone of a wide variety of mammals must be approximately the same. It is recognized that at least in comparison with carnivores and other primates, man is, in most respects, a relatively puny mammal, in spite of the fact that many men are heavily muscled. Experiments to test the strength of anthropoid apes have not been particularly satisfactory, but it has been ascertained with seeming conclusiveness that a chimpanzee of moderate size can perform certain feats necessitating strength several hundred per cent greater than can a man with muscles of equal or even greater bulk (see Bauman, 1926). The muscles of the ape may well be in better physical condition than could be attained by those of a man, but it is maintained that most of such instances of supremacy in strength are due to the fact that the nervous tone is far better developed than that of man could ever be—in short, that the nervous stimuli received by the muscles of certain very "strong" mammals are more comparable to those of the man who exhibits "demoniacal strength" during seizures of one sort or another.

Still another aspect of muscle action must be considered. A wisp of a man, with spindly legs, may leap well over six feet high, although in other ways he may be woefully lacking in strength. Another man, strong, well-muscled, and weighing 175 pounds may jump just as high. The former individual exhibits no general indications of superior nervous tone. It is possible that the nervous tone of his leg muscles may be superior to the average while that of his other muscles is not, but it is more probable that the chief reason for his proficiency in jumping is due to the better coordination of all muscles that can be of help in swift extension of the leg and foot.

Analogous cases concerning a variety of mammals may be called to mind. The hind legs of a jumping mouse of the genus *Zapus* can administer little sledge-hammer blows as if the limbs were released by a trigger, while those of the mole, although actually stronger, can kick but feebly, because the animal has used its hind limbs merely for slow progression and for bracing its body while digging. There is no physical quality that we can see to account for such great variation in the muscular action of these two mammals, although there is naturally great difference in conformation, that in the length of the bones being more properly a result— not a cause. The muscles are essentially the same in texture, but in one there is coordination of the nerve impulses and consequent action for speed, and in the other, for strength most efficient for certain work to be performed.

In man the limbs are normally parallel to the body axis, and the muscles, at rest and in action, have become adapted to this position. It can readily be seen that in most other mammals, whose limbs are normally at right angles to the body axis, different muscle action results. Regarding just what this comprises we are usually in ignorance. A well known case in point is that the upper portion of the serratus magnus can be flexed in man while the arm is in any position, but the lower part can be brought into use only when the humerus is at an angle of more than 45 degrees to the body. In the case of one of the lower mammals, whose normal position of the limbs is different than in man, these facts are hardly likely to be the same.

A muscle may be a prime agent in one or two movements, but it may also assist in varying degree during a great number of other movements. Also it is well known that a muscle possible of two different functions may be paralysed for one but not for the other. The next logical step from this is to the deduction that a muscle may be capable of certain action in one mammal for which it is normally "paralysed" or inhibited in another.

As further illustrating differing functions of the same muscle, it may be mentioned, as discussed later, that in a mammal with tibia and fibula fused, the muscles which in man are employed for supination and pronation of the lower leg may, and in fact must, be used largely for a different purpose.

The principles involved in the lever action of the different classes of muscles may be ascertained from numerous text books, but they will not here be discussed. The investigation of the lever power of the various muscles would be of much value in the present connection, but the attachments of most of the muscles are relatively so broad that the decision for an exact point of insertion would be largely arbitrary, and especially in the case of a subject as small as the wood rat, the necessary percentage of error in the calculations would be so large as to render the results valueless or actually misleading. This is unfortunate, for relatively slight differences in the leverages exerted by many muscles are productive of very great variation in actional results.

It will be seen from the foregoing statements what numerous and complex factors are concerned in the actions of muscles. It is necessary, therefore, to employ the utmost caution and conservatism in making assertions regarding the exact part that they play in the economy of any mammal. For this reason any attempt to compare the strength of a particular muscle in terms solely of its cubic capacity, such as was done by Holliger (1916) in the case of the pocket gopher, a ground squirrel, and a rabbit, is misleading. It can be only after much patient research and a consideration of extensive data that any such comparisons can constitute anything more than guess work.

In considering coordination between groups of muscles it should be understood that muscular action is of three kinds—shortening, static, and lengthening action. During the act of leaping certain muscles sharply contract, it is necessary that others be lengthened, while still others perform static work, as holding the body rigid or exerting force to prevent undesired movements. The lengthening of the muscles concerned is not passive nor caused merely by the contraction of the opposing muscles, but is a true inhibitional stimulus of the muscles, which removes the normal tone. Every strong or especially quick movement necessitates the employment of these three sorts of action. There is also selective coordination between two or more actional results. This is illustrated by the fact that if one reclines, he may at will raise the legs vertically, or sit up with equal facility. Static contractions are employed when one stands, or holds a weight stationary, or holds the body rigid for the better performance of some other movement. The same amount of muscular energy may be accomplished as in violent

motion, but no useful work is directly performed. Oppositional contractions are somewhat similar, and equally necessary in daily life. They are needed in controlling the actions
of other muscles.

This brings us to the question of group variation in
oppositional and inhibitional stimuli, touched upon previously. It falls under the general head of coordination
between muscles and groups of muscles. Such variation
must be great, but its satisfactory investigation in the
lower Mammalia seems almost impossible. The Impalla
(*Æpyceros*) of Africa makes frequent leaps of as much as
thirty-five feet, considerably surpassing those made by
any other of its relatives. There is probably no gross,
anatomical feature to account for this ability that is not
shared by similar species of like conformation. This phenomenal leaping ability is likely attributable to an unusually
efficient quality of stimuli transmitted to the motor endings
of the nerves, superior coordination between all muscles that
can be of possible aid in violent extension of the hind limbs,
or a greater facility in inhibitional and oppositional control
of the muscles which might hinder such movements. The
last point is probably not sufficient in itself to account for
such great leaps, and the reason is probably a harmonious
combination of the three features mentioned.

The head muscles of a mammal have developed in response
to phylogenetic stimuli and those concerned with food habits
and dentitional causes. These, of course, vary widely with
the group to which a particular mammal belongs, and usually
are negligibly subject to the influences which have been
brought to bear in the case of mammals which exhibit
parallelism and convergence for best coping with a particular
mode of life especially as regards progression. To a lesser
extent is this the case with the neck muscles. Burrowing
mammals of widely dissimilar affinities may use the head as
a modified shovel, for instance, which markedly affects the

cervical musculature. The neck may be lengthened or shortened for particular reasons, or it may have to support unusual weight, as in the moose or elephant. The muscles of the neck often show great variation, of much value to the anatomist, but such specialization is not easily correlated, as a rule, with diverse modes of locomotion. Ordinarily the muscles of the back are employed largely for static work, as stiffeners of the vertebral column in the various positions which the latter may assume. In the case of those mammals capable of prodigious leaps the body acts as a fulcrum upon which work the levers of the limbs, and its musculature may be accordingly modified secondarily to a very significant degree; or in such a long-bodied and short-legged animal as the weasel the back-bone and its musculature may constitute an important, primary aid to locomotion. The more distal portion of the tail muscles in animals in which this member is non-prehensile usually has few characters of much interest to us. Save in the kangaroos and in aquatic mammals, the tail is seldom used to exert real force of any kind, but only as a balancer to maintain necessary equilibrium of its owner, and the muscles at the base of the tail are used to perform the movements corollary to this.

It is in the leg muscles that we should expect to find the greatest direct indications of varied life habits, and significant similarities in such as exhibit convergence toward marked specialization of a particular nature. Few details of an animal may be said to be unnecessary for its continued existence, of course, but as concerns its own sum of characters, it is upon its ability to travel about in the manner most suitable to its ecologic position that its survival as a species chiefly depends. Therefore it is in the leg muscles, especially of those mammals that are well fitted for particular modes of locomotion, that we are primarily interested.

Forty to sixty years ago there was much philosophical discussion by such men as Agassiz, Oken, Owen and Wilder concerning possible morphologic homology between the anterior and posterior portions of the vertebrate body. Some rather fanciful arguments were then presented pro and con, but the matter has been accorded practically no attention in more recent times. Consideration of this subject can be adequately given only by one who has a very extensive knowledge of the anatomy of the lower vertebrates, which the present writer has not, and his only purpose in bringing up the subject is to emphasize the fact that there are many interesting points for comparison between the fore and hind limbs of mammals the consideration of which one may do well to approach with an open mind. It is not necessary that the theory of antero-posterior symmetry be accepted but merely that we note the significance of the evidence of correspondence that is presented as regards the muscles of the fore and hind limbs.

As expressing the relationship between certain muscles of either extremity, homologue is a term that seems too strong, while analogue is too weak. Correspondence and counterpart would perhaps be better for designating the agreement of a muscle in one leg with another particular muscle of the opposite extremity.

As is well known, any such correspondence as exists is between *opposite* muscles, as between the muscles craniad of the humerus and caudad of the femur. And, broadly speaking, sets of muscles situated contiguously proximad and distad are alternately flexors and extensors or vice versa. This is morphologically due to the fact that the alternate segments of a limb are inclined alternately craniad and caudad. The distal extremities of the scapula and ilium[1]

---

[1] As previously mentioned, these two bones are usually considered as having their morphological relationship with the trunk, but most of the muscles connected with them are more intimately concerned with the limbs, and as they constitute frameworks for the support of appendageous muscles, they will be treated as segments of their respective limbs.

diverge from the center of the trunk, the humerus and femur converge, while the forearm and lower leg diverge once more. The foot proper is also inclined forward, while the tendency of the toes is to bend rearward. The hand or fore foot seems to present an anomaly to this line of reasoning, for it, too, is inclined forward, but this is an adaptational modification and its present position was not originally fundamental. It must be remembered that the primal position of the limbs was lateral, with the feet extended laterad instead of craniad. A rearward inclination of the fore foot would obviously constitute a modification impractical in a quadruped; so the rotation of the forearm and change to a forward inclination of the hand was forced during the evolution of the Mammalia coincident with the abandonment of the purely lateral extension of the limbs. This is illustrated in the development of embryos, for in the early stages the radius and ulna are parallel, while later the hand is pronated and there are changes in the wrist to fit the position of the fore foot which has proved to be structurally advantageous. In man and such other mammals as have no rigid articulation of the radius and ulna, the preadaptational position of the hand may be assumed at will, or almost so. It will then be apparent that in this position the muscles which raise the hand towards the arm act as flexors rather than extensors as normally termed, and that considered as counterparts, the flexors of the hand must be treated as corresponding to the extensors of the foot, and vice versa.

Before one could be qualified to present an authoritative opinion regarding the theory of antero-posterior symmetry as affecting the limbs he would be obliged to do a vast amount of research on the subject. Concerning this the writer offers no opinion one way or the other. There are several objections to this thesis but they do not seem to be insurmountable. Even though there be no true homology between the anterior and posterior extremities, the reasons for accepting the hypothesis of a teleological connection between the two seem sufficiently trustworthy for acceptance, and it furnishes us with a very desirable basis for the comparison of the functioning of the limbs. In an ideally generalized vertebrate the fore leg and hind leg would have equal power, and the flexors and extensors of each would be respectively of the same strength as those of the other; or because of the mechanical differences presented by variations in the structure of the shoulder and pelvic regions, it would be better to state that the limbs would be capable of the same effective work. It is probable that there is no living mammal so primitive as to approach such a

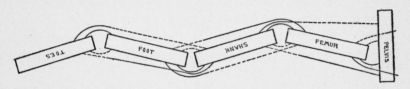

FIG. 36. Schematic diagram of simplified muscular plan for the five segments of the right hind limb, illustrating flexors and extensors. Broken line flexor action, solid line extensor action.

generalized type. The genus *Neotoma* is, of course, far more specialized; but it is nevertheless sufficiently generalized for our purpose.

The legs, then, from a myological viewpoint are each composed of five segments: the first comprises the clavicle and scapula, or the pelvis; the second the humerus or femur; the third the radius and ulna, or tibia and fibula; the fourth the carpus and metacarpus, or tarsus and metatarsus; and the fifth the digits. The metacarpals and metatarsals are usually treated under the same heading as the digits, but from a functional standpoint they constitute a part of the carpus or tarsus, respectively.

The diagrammatically simplified plan of musculature for each segment of a limb is a long, direct flexor and extensor, inserted upon the bone and originating from the second segment above; a short, direct flexor and extensor, inserted upon the bone and originating from the segment next above; and an indirect flexor and extensor, originating upon the segment next above and inserted upon the one next below (see fig. 36). In actual practice, of course, the simplified scheme for the fourth and fifth segments, with the several tarsal and digital elements, would be much more complex than this. No such schematic plan for adductors and abductors can be given, for although all joints are capable of extension and flexion, comparatively few allow extensive adduction and abduction.

So far as I am aware, the above plan is never met with in actual practice, for anatomical complications, following the need for complex actions, has been forced far beyond such simplicity. In many cases it is possible to state which are the primary long, short, and indirect flexors or extensors, but usually the musculature has become so specialized, in even the lowest mammals, so split up and changed, that muscles which really should be classed as accessory may often be as important as true primary ones, while the functions of others have changed entirely; so that in the present stage of the technique on the subject, it behooves one to be conservative in making statements. A qualifying phrase of caution can not accompany each item hereafter mentioned, without proving tedious, however, so it must be understood that the muscle facts and actions given are merely what *seems* to be so, from an examination of the material. The following tables have been prepared after a careful study of the positions of the muscles in the genus *Neotoma*, with due regard to the functions of the same muscles in man and the cat. Their functions, as stated, repre-

sent only what they apparently *can* do in the wood rat.
When a muscle appears to have but slight or doubtful
function, the fact is shown by its enclosure in brackets.
Rotation, as of the femur, is not indicated, nor can the many
slight, associational uses be considered in the present
connection.

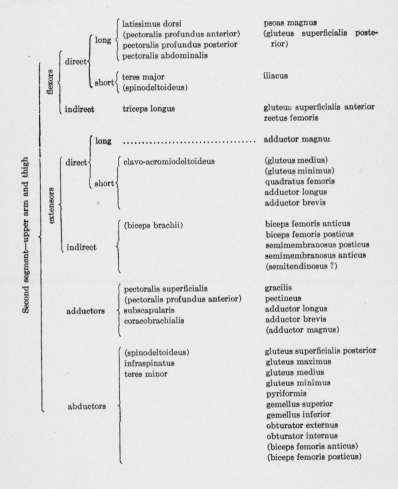

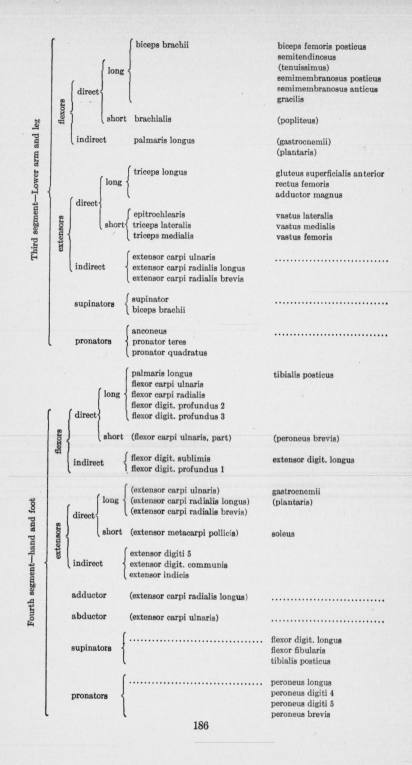

Third segment—Lower arm and leg

flexors
  direct
    long
      biceps brachii   biceps femoris posticus
                                        semitendinosus
                                        (tenuissimus)
                                        semimembranosus posticus
                                        semimembranosus anticus
                                        gracilis
    short brachialis   (popliteus)
  indirect palmaris longus   (gastrocnemii)
                                        (plantaris)

extensors
  direct
    long
      triceps longus   gluteus superficialis anterior
                                        rectus femoris
                                        adductor magnus
    short
      epitrochlearis   vastus lateralis
      triceps lateralis   vastus medialis
      triceps medialis   vastus femoris
  indirect
      extensor carpi ulnaris   ....
      extensor carpi radialis longus
      extensor carpi radialis brevis

supinators
      supinator   ....
      biceps brachii

pronators
      anconeus   ....
      pronator teres
      pronator quadratus

flexors
  direct
    long
      palmaris longus   tibialis posticus
      flexor carpi ulnaris
      flexor carpi radialis
      flexor digit. profundus 2
      flexor digit. profundus 3
    short (flexor carpi ulnaris, part) (peroneus brevis)
  indirect
      flexor digit. sublimis   extensor digit. longus
      flexor digit. profundus 1

Fourth segment—hand and foot

extensors
  direct
    long
      (extensor carpi ulnaris)   gastrocnemii
      (extensor carpi radialis longus) (plantaris)
      (extensor carpi radialis brevis)
    short (extensor metacarpi pollicis) soleus
  indirect
      extensor digiti 5
      extensor digit. communis
      extensor indicis

adductor (extensor carpi radialis longus) ....

abductor (extensor carpi ulnaris)   ....

supinators ....   flexor digit. longus
                                            flexor fibularis
                                            tibialis posticus

pronators ....   peroneus longus
                                            peroneus digiti 4
                                            peroneus digiti 5
                                            peroneus brevis

186

		flexor digit. sublimis	plantaris
	flexors	flexor digit. profundus	flexor digit. longus
Fifth seg-ment—fin-gers and toes			flexor fibularis
		extensor digiti 5	extensor hallucis
	extensors	extensor digit. communis	extensor digit. longus
		extensor indicis	peroneus digiti 4
			peroneus digiti 5

Most muscles, at least of the more proximal segments, can by virtue of their position do two things. They can either flex or extend, and at the same time adduct or abduct or rotate; but they can act in but one direction as can a rubber band stretched between two points. When the origins are not immovably fixed they can, however, move both bones to which they are attached. Of the above class are the short, direct, flexor and extensor muscles. The long muscles of the limbs, however, can act in at least two ways. Each muscle of this sort is controlled by two associates, one of origin and one of insertion, and an antagonist of origin and one of insertion. By the aid of these four, short muscles, the long one can act in two ways. When two of the short ones are flexed, the long one may be made to flex one segment, while when the two alternate short ones act, the long one extends the adjoining segment. Theoretically a long muscle, if a flexor of the upper segment, acts as an extensor of the one next distad, and vice versa. In actual practice the modifications of its position may be such as largely to inhibit one movement. Thus, certain long muscles of the lower arm may be able to cause no appreciable movements of that segment, and in *Neotoma* it is doubtful if the long semitendinosus, which flexes the shank, has an appreciable effect upon the thigh. On the other hand, the biceps brachii in man may flex and supinate the forearm, and extend and abduct the femur. It is true that the abduction is but slight, but it can really be said to have four actions, two of them supplementary to the others.

As the pelvis is immovably fixed while the scapula is not,

there are bound to be certain basic, functional differences found between the fore and hind limbs. The scapula, and through it the entire arm, may be moved in various directions, assisting, from a mechanical viewpoint, especially in adduction, abduction and rotation of the whole arm. Hence there are notably few adductors and abductors operating directly upon the humerus or second segment. The ones present are not lacking in strength, but the mobility of the scapula precludes the necessity for very many muscles transmitting a complexity of movement to the humerus such as is needed by the femur.

It will also be noted that the flexors of the humerus are many, while the femur has few, and that the extensors of the former are few, while the latter has many. This is, of course, natural, the arrangement being conducive to the strength needed in locomotion, during which the humerus is flexed while the femur is extended. There are probably few actions in the life of the average mammal necessitating strong extension of the arm. All that is really needed is sufficient strength for quick recovery to overcome inertia following flexion of this member. Quickness would be of greater advantage than power, and for the former the extensor muscles of the humerus are excellently placed. The flexors of the femur seem to be more powerful than the extensors of the humerus, as discussed shortly.

The flexors of the third segment or forearm are notably few as compared to those of the lower leg. This fact, too, conforms to our expectations. Both the long and short direct flexors are of moderate size, and but a fraction of the bulk of the triceps series, which is the muscle mass for extension antagonistic to the biceps and its accessory, the brachialis. These facts make for added proficiency in running, climbing, digging and such work. Several muscles which might be expected to constitute indirect flexors of the forearm probably have no such action, or to an inappreciable extent. The structure of an elbow joint of this character presents a number of anomalies. For one teleological reason or another, many muscles take origin from the humerus, instead of from one of the bones distally adjacent. The position of the origins upon the epicondyles makes it impossible for some of them to exert leverage upon the forearm, and to all intents their functions seem to be largely the same as though origin were from the forearm itself. One effect of the humeral origin of these muscles is to add strength to the adjoining articulation at the elbow, and it may be presumed that such strengthening is not a purely fortuitous result. It should be noted that when the arm is relaxed, the angle of the forearm with the humerus is not almost 180 degrees, as in man, but in a fresh specimen after rigor mortis had passed, about 135 degrees, although this angle was exceeded when considerable force was applied. This position gives greater leverage to the muscles, especially the flexors, of the forearm.

The actions of the hand or fourth segment are exceedingly complex, with the many bones and multitude of tendons whose functions are interdependent to a high degree. Both the flexors and extensors are many, though some of them act as such to a relatively insignificant extent. Although the wrist joint is capable of practically no rotation per se, the possible rotation of the forearm coupled with the interplay between the bones of the carpus gives to the hand about the same amount of sidewise movement or rotation as in man. Possible supination seems to be about 90 degrees from the vertical, or half that in man, while possible movement in pronation is but a few degrees beyond the horizontal. The mobility of the hand must therefore be considered as only moderate in the genus *Neotoma*. It must be remembered that the extensors of the hand are morphologically comparable to the flexors of the foot, and the former are considerably weaker than the "flexors" of the carpus.

The weakness of the smaller muscles of the fore foot and digits, coupled with the fact that the pollex is non-functional, implies only a moderate amount of facility in digital movements. Flexion and extension of the latter are adequately strong, but as a true hand, the extremity of the fore leg is not highly accomplished.

The functional length of the fore limb in the genus *Neotoma* is only about two-thirds that of the hind leg. The former member is used to a considerable extent as a tool during the normal activity of the animal, this constituting an important secondary use. Its primary use is, of course, for locomotion, but even during this function it need do little but support the anterior portion of the body, while the hind limbs can furnish practically all of the driving power if necessary. As the importance during locomotion of the fore limbs decreases, so will their size (unless stimulated by other hard work), and this, naturally, is followed by a compensating increase in locomotional importance and relative size of the hind limbs.

The pelvis must be considered as, functionally, the first segment of the hind limb, corresponding to the scapula, although the former is immovably fused to the vertebral column. Strength of a certain sort could be secured by an increase in the size of the muscles without such fusion, but rigidity of support is perhaps requisite to the efficiency displayed by the hind limbs in swift locomotion and the proper performance of many of the other feats which these members are called upon to execute in daily life. As the pelvis is immovable, all adduction, abduction, and rotation of the leg must be through the femur, which is rendered possible by its ball-and-socket joint with the pelvis. Practically all muscles governing such actions must therefore arise from the pelvis or its vicinity, and most of them are inserted upon the femoral segment, although several extend to the lower leg.

In such a mammal as the wood rat the primary function of the hind limb is locomotion, necessitating chiefly flexion and extension of that member. In reviewing the action of running it is seen that the first step is the flexion of the femur, accompanied by slight flexion of the lower leg, foot and toes. In man, just before the culmination of the forward thrust of the knee, there is extension of the lower leg, foot and toes, rapidly followed by extension of the femur, flexion of the lower leg that is slight in degree but strong in action through the hamstring muscles, extension of the foot and flexion of the toes. At the culmination of the rearward motion, there is again a tendency toward extension of the segments below the knee. In man, however, the muscles are adaptationally modified to fit his normal posture. The latter, it must be recollected, comprises extension of the femur to a greater degree than it is perhaps possible for the rat to assume, and full extension of the lower leg. In such a position, could the rat adopt it, the muscles extending from the ilium to the leg would have but little leverage, while those from the inferior tuberosity of the ischium and the superficial muscles in this region that pass to the lower leg would lose most of their efficacy.

In running, a lack of power, or more properly speed, in the flexors of the femur and extensors of the lower leg may be almost as fatal to great swiftness as a similar lack in the driving muscles of the leg. Some fast sprinters are such by grace of the power of their driving muscles, enabling them to cover an unusual distance at each stride. Others are so by reason of the strength of the antagonist muscles, allowing phenomenally quick recovery after each step, and so enabling them to take unusually rapid, though short, strides. And we can all remember, when we were boys, running down hill and attaining such speed that a fall ensued because of our inability to work our legs faster. In a mammal exhibiting saltatorial adaptations, the recovery muscles, comprising

the flexors of the femur and extensors of the lower leg, need
not be so efficient, for there is ample time during long leaps
for slow recovery between impulses.   In a relatively short-
legged mammal, however, which normally takes short steps,
quick recovery is important, and the muscles concerned
must be powerful.   Such is the case—especially in view of the
normal position of the femur—with the psoas magnus, iliacus,
gluteus superficialis anterior and rectus femoris which are
the muscles of chief use in flexing the thigh, and with the
extensor muscles of the lower leg, especially the vasti, or
short extensors.

In the normal standing position of the rat the femur and
lower leg are sharply flexed, to a degree rather comparable
to the corresponding segments of a man when he is squatting
or crouched.   This static posture gives great leverage to
the muscles extending from the long ilium, and from the
caudally extended inferior tuberosity of the ischium through
the more superficial flexors extending far down the lower
leg, such as the biceps femoris, gracilis, and semitendinosus.
A similar position for the last three muscles is entirely impossible for a mammal with static posture comparable to that
of man.

In rapid locomotion of the wood rat the arc described by
the femur probably does not much exceed 90, and is certainly
less than 120 degrees.   As the static position of this bone is
almost parallel to the vertebral axis, its rearward swing
would be but little more than vertical to this axis, and, as
previously mentioned, its flexor and extensor muscles are
excellently placed for efficacy in this position.   As is necessary, the extensors of the femur are much more powerful
and numerous than are those of the humerus, or than the
actionally comparable flexors of the latter, for the hind leg
is much the more important in locomotion.

In the case of the fore leg, inhibitional, tendinous action
of the two-joint muscles is not marked.   The forearm may

be flexed or extended when the humerus is in any position, and similarly with the hand in relation to the remainder of the arm. This is not the case, however, with the hind leg.

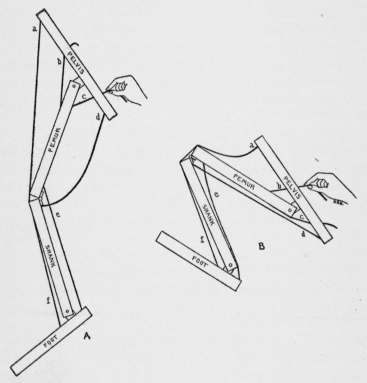

FIG. 37. Illustration of the tendinous and tonal action of the two-joint flexors and extensors of the hind limb (partially after Bowen). (a) Rectus femoris and gluteus superficialis anterior; (b) psoas magnus (long) and iliacus (short); (c) adductor magnus (long), adductores longus and brevis, quadratus femoris, glutei medius and minimus (short); (d) biceps, semimembranosus, semitendinosus, gracilis; (e) gastrocnemii and plantaris; (f) tibialis anticus.

When the femur is flexed, the tibia can not be extended more than to an angle of about 120 degrees with the thigh. When the latter is extended, the lower leg can also be fully extended. The foot probably *can* be extended when the leg is in any position, but only with an effort when the two more proximal segments are flexed.

The muscle action controlling this state of affairs is as follows (see fig. 37): When the long (psoas magnus) and short (iliacus) flexors of the thigh operate, the two-joint extensors of the lower leg (gluteus superficialis anterior and rectus femoris) are relaxed, but the corresponding flexors of this segment (the three adductors, two lesser glutei, and quadratus femoris) are under tension, which tends to flex the lower leg. At the same time, the two-joint extensors of the foot (the gastrocnemii and plantaris) are relaxed. Theoretically the long extensor digitorum should in this position exert a tendinous action to flex the foot, but such is not now the case. Instead, the tibialis anticus has sufficient tone so that it definitely flexes the foot when the normal tension of the gastrocnemii is removed by means of flexion of the lower leg. This tonal contraction of the tibialis anticus is evidently not sufficiently pronounced so that it is impossible for the animal to extend the foot when the remainder of the leg is flexed, but it is ample for the involuntary recovery or flexion of the foot following extension of this segment during the act of running. This tonal action of the anterior tibial muscle is not apparent in man, he probably having lost it (if he ever had it) as a result of his erect posture. It may be readily seen that involuntary flexion of the foot while a man is running is not of importance, but that in such an animal as the wood rat, which runs in a somewhat crouching posture, it is of consequence that the longer foot be automatically and safely flexed during recovery of the leg to prevent it from dragging on the ground.

As discussed shortly, the foot is capable of no rotation per se, and yet functional rotation of this member is necessary in the economy of the animal. This is accomplished by rotation of the whole leg, and for this reason the muscles—

chiefly the obturators, pyriformis, gemelli, and to some extent the quadratus femoris—which act as rotators of the femur must be efficient.

It will be noted that the distal extremity of the femur is vastly different from that of the humerus. It must be stronger, with a heavier articulation to withstand lateral stress, and it must be of a decidedly different form to accommodate the broad head of the tibia, rather than the peculiarities of the radial and ulnar articulations. Partly because of these facts and probably because of the differences in function between the lower leg and arm, there are not as many muscles originating from the epicondyles of the femur as from those of the humerus, more of them arising from the heads of the tibia and fibula, and hence, presenting a simpler, less specialized condition.

Analogous to the relationship of the olecranon with the ulna is that of the patella with the tibia, although the latter is a separate bone. It is by means of the patella and its ligament that the three vasti and three other direct flexors of the lower leg operate. Due to their efficiency and the normally flexed, static position of this segment, it now has no indirect extensor operating as such.

The static position of the lower leg or third segment is at an angle of less than 90 degrees with the femur, and its functional arc of motion while the animal is running in its normal, crouching posture is therefore probably greater than in man, although *possible* arc of motion in the latter is evidently no smaller. The tibia can assume a position on a line with the femur, but it is doubtful if this segment is extended to the utmost during any part of the stride, although it is conceivable that this may be the case at the culmination of the rearward swing. Flexor muscles attached to it as in man would be very inefficient and many of them are therefore placed well down upon the lower leg. Notwithstanding such attachment the shank may be fully extended and these flexors therefore have great elasticity. The ones with most proximal attachment to the shank are probably of considerably less use in flexion of this segment than in extension of the femur, but the more distal ones, by virtue of their insertions and the position of the bones, can exert great force in flexion of the lower leg, and such action is of far more importance to this animal while running than can the corresponding motion be to man. In fact, it may play almost as important a part in this as does the extension of the femur. It will, then, be seen that the direct flexors concerned with this portion of the leg are extraordinarily efficient, and much larger as well as more numerous than are those of the forearm, the latter having less need for strength. The indirect flexors the (gastrocnemii and plantaris), however, seem to operate very slightly as such. As the tibia and fibula are solidly fused, there can, of course, be no pronation and supination of this segment.

Also due to the fact that there can be no rotation of the lower leg in *Neotoma*, and because articulation with the foot is by a single bone instead of two, thus reducing play, only a negligible amount of rotation of this, the fourth segment, is possible. But the foot must assume a great variety of positions, as any one will realize who has observed a wood rat endeavoring to escape from a trap. Hence, necessary rotation of the foot must be accomplished by a rotation of the whole leg at the hip joint, and both the myological and osteological features allow a great amount of such movement.

Possible supination exceeds the average in man, for it is possible for the "ball" of the foot to be placed at an angle of slightly more than 90 degrees to the horizontal. Pronation also greatly exceeds what is possible in the foot of man, and the "ball" of the foot, although of course not the heel, may assume in this direction an angle of about 75 degrees to the horizontal. Examination of a cleaned skeleton sheds little light on the reason for this. It is probably due chiefly to a greater amount of freedom of movement between the bones of the tarsus, and an adaptational arrangement of the ligaments, the whole facilitated by the form of the articular surfaces of the lower leg and the astragalus.

The muscles flexing the foot, corresponding, it will be recalled, to the extensors of the hand, are but three in number and weak. The extensors, however, although but four, are exceedingly powerful. The pedal extremity, being of fair proportions for a generalized mammal, constitutes a decided aid during rapid locomotion, especially as an accessory to the somewhat flexed lower leg. The structure of the gastrocnemii as well as the size of the entire Achillean muscle mass composed of these two, the plantaris and soleus, operating upon the extension of the calcaneum, constitute an exceedingly powerful group for extension of the foot. Pronation of the foot, by means of the peronei, is strong, enabling this member to recover smartly after supination. The two movements act antagonistically to preserve a proper balance.

As in the hand, the flexors of the toes, are strong, while the extensors are much weaker. The extensor digitorum longus is the only general extensor of the digits, and the chief function of this seems to be as a flexor of the foot, for when this work is performed, the force applied to extend the toes is so slight that it is more than overcome by the flexors, which in this position of the digits are mechanically tensed.

The toes may be considered as having moderate grasping power. As the foot is well supplied with small muscles, and the hallux can be opposed to as great an angle as 90 degrees, the animal can make good use of these members in negotiating slender twigs or performing other similar work. The chief function of these muscles, however, is undoubtedly to increase the strength of the foot as a whole and bind the separate bones into a single unit.

DISCUSSION OF SUBGENERIC VARIATION

A tabular comparison (table 1) is offered of those muscles which exhibit relative differences between the three subgenera.   Obviously it is practical to indicate these only in a general way.   In addition it must be borne in mind that a number of them may be apparent rather than real, for the specimens of *Teonoma* dissected were much larger than the others and nice decision of an impossible degree of exactitude was often necessary in order properly to decide whether a myological difference encountered was relative or due merely to the discrepancy in size between the individuals compared.

In addition, there are differences in the degree of ease with which certain muscles are separable from their neighbors, as well as others which as far as we can see have no functional variation, as in the precise conformation of such muscles as the rectus abdominis, mentioned under the proper headings.

It will be noted from the table that if *Homodontomys* be arbitrarily considered as the normal type with which to compare the other two subgenera, *Teonoma* lies at the other extreme, on the whole showing the widest departure in characters, while *Neotoma* occupies a position between the two.   The last is either intermediate or resembles one or other of the remaining subgenera in 42 of the 48 myological points in which there is subgeneric variation.   In 24 cases it is nearer *Homodontomys*, in 13 nearer *Teonoma*, while in 5 instances it is fairly intermediate between the two.   In but 6 cases out of these 48 is *Neotoma* more extreme in any particular than the two others.   The platysma, rhomboideus anterior, pectoralis abdominalis, and sternocostalis are smallest or weakest in this subgenus, the panniculus carnosus is heaviest, while the two bellies of the digastricus are most distinct.   In none of these 48 is the development the same in *Homodontomys* as in *Teonoma*.

Most of the differences indicated are but slight, and in

TABLE 1

SUMMARY OF MYOLOGICAL VARIATIONS IN THE SUBGENERA OF *Neotoma*

MUSCLE	HOMODONTOMYS	NEOTOMA	TEONOMA
Of facial skin.............	norm	norm	heavier
Platysma.................	norm	lighter	heavier
Sternofascialis............	present	absent	absent
Temporalis...............	norm	larger	largest
Digastricus..............	norm	norm; 2 bellies more distinct	larger; 2 bellies less distinct
Stylohyoideus............	norm	larger	largest
Sternomastoideus.........	norm	larger	larger
Cleidomastoideus.........	norm	norm	larger
Omohyoideus.............	norm	larger	larger
Scalenus (med.)..........	from ribs 3 and 4	from ribs 4 and 5	from ribs 5 and 6
Scalenus (vent.)..........	from ribs 3, 4, and 5	from ribs 4 and 5	from ribs 4 and 5
Longus colli..............	norm	norm	larger
Longus capitis............	mid. 5 cerv. vert.	mid. 5 cerv. vert.	last 6 cerv. vert.
Panniculus carnosus......	norm	heavier	lighter
Pectoralis superfic........	norm	norm	heavier
Pectoralis profundus.....	norm	norm	heavier
Pectoralis abdominalis...	norm	weaker	more triangular
Serratus magnus..........	norm	norm	broader
Levator scapulae.........	norm	norm	broader
Sternocostalis............	norm	smaller	largest
Obliq. abdom. externus...	norm	larger	larger
Acromiotrapezius.........	norm	norm	origin broader
Spinotrapezius............	norm	weaker	weaker
Latissimus dorsi..........	norm	norm	larger
Rhomboideus anticus.....	norm	smaller	largest
Serratus post. superior...	norm	weaker	weaker
Splenius.................	norm	larger	origin broader
Iliocostales..............	norm	norm	smaller
Biventer cervicis (post.)..	from 3 and 4 to 6 or 7 thoracics	from 3 and 4 to 6 or 7 thoracics	from 4 and 5 to 7 or 8 thoracics
Biventer cervicis (ant.)...	from 3 thoracic to axis	from 3 thoracic to axis	from 5 thoracic to 4 or 3 cervical

TABLE 1—*Continued*

MUSCLE	HOMODONTOMYS	NEOTOMA	TEONOMA
Complexus	from last 3 cervs.	from last 3 cerv.	from last cerv. and thoracic 1 and 2
Rect. cap. lateralis	norm	smaller	smaller
Longus atlantis	from cerv. 3, 4 and 5	from cerv. 3, 4 and 5	from cerv. 3 and 4
Extens. caud. medialis	norm	norm	larger
Acromiodeltoideus	norm	norm	larger
Teres minor	norm	larger	larger
Epitrochlearis	norm	norm	larger
Triceps longus	norm	norm	broader
Flex digit. sublimis	norm; 3 tendons	norm; 3 tendons	larger; 4 tendons
Extens. digit. commun	norm	norm	larger
Psoas minor	norm	origin broader	origin broader
Glut. superfic. anter	norm	norm	larger
Gluteus maximus	norm	broader	broader
Gemellus superior	norm	norm	broader
Gracilis	norm	larger	largest
Adductor magnus	insertion pierced	insertion partly separated	insertion completely separated
Gastrocnemius lateralis	norm	ental aponeurosis simpler	ental aponeurosis simpler
Peroneus digiti 4	insertion single	insertion single	insertion double

addition, many of these muscles play a relatively minor rôle in the economy of the animals. Hence, a more detailed consideration of each point of difference is hardly worth while; but certain trends that seem to be apparent should be discussed.

Directly correlated with myological variations are osteological differences, or at least many of them. Certain of the latter are undoubtedly attributable to causes other than the direct influences of the muscles. There are certain hereditary characters of one sort or another, such as long-face or broad-face in man, which vary irrespective of the muscles, and a number of other instances may be recalled. Nevertheless, in considering comparative differences between groups of mammals as closely related as are the three subgenera of wood rats, it seems logical to consider that but a small proportion of the osteological variation is due to stimuli other than myological, although some of these have been indirect, while others were direct.

It has been claimed above that the largest muscles need not always be the strongest. In a comparison of mammals of such near relationship, it is to be expected that most muscles of one subgenus are usually, but not always, strictly comparable with the same muscles of the others on size alone. If a process or ridge upon which muscles are attached is more prominent in one subgenus, it is extremely likely that this is because the attached muscles are either stronger, or what amounts to the same thing, better situated for the work to be performed by them. Hence, because it was not apparent during dissection that a muscle of one animal was larger than the same muscle of another, it should not be deemed that appreciable difference in the process to which it was attached is without important myological import.

For the purpose of comparing the significance of the myological differences with the osteologial ones, a condensed table (table 2) of the latter is here presented. As with the table for muscular variations, *Homodontomys* is arbitrarily selected as the basic type with which to compare the other two subgenera. Some of the differences listed are too slight to be of definite import to us, while others, perhaps of greater consequence, are not included in the table because of their complexity.

Many of the differences of percentages in the table immediately preceding are too slight to be of value for they are not greater than the coefficient of error; but the correlation of some of these differences and the trends shown thereby are highly interesting and significant.

TABLE 2

SUMMARY OF OSTEOLOGICAL VARIATIONS IN THE SUBGENERA OF WOOD RATS

OSTEOLOGICAL DETAIL	HOMODONTOMYS	NEOTOMA	TEONOMA
Skull			
Width, ant. zygoma....	norm	narrower	narrowest
Width, post. zygoma...	norm	wider	widest
Septa zygomatica.......	norm	norm	smaller
Temporal ridge and fossa.................	norm	larger	largest
Pterygoid fossa.........	norm:norm	wider:deeper	wider: norm
Mastoid proc. squamos.	norm	norm	larger
Coronoid process.......	norm	norm	larger
Angular process........	norm	longer	longer
Transv. mandib. fossa..	norm	larger	largest
Hyoid...................	norm	norm	larger
Cervical vert............	norm	shorter	norm
Anter. spine of axis....	norm	higher	lower
Infer. lamella of 6th....	norm	smallest	smaller
Thoracic vert............	norm	longest	longer
Spines of 3d and 4th...	norm	norm	longer
Spines of thoracic type .	to 10th	to 9th	to 9th
Lumbar vert..............	norm	shorter	shorter
Postzygapoph. small...	6th	5th and 6th	5th and 6th
Hypapophyses.........	norm	lower	lower
Sacral vert..............	norm	longer	longer
Size...................	norm	norm	broader
Diapophyses...........	poster. > anter.	poster. > anter	poster. = anter.
Caudal vert..............	av. no. 30.4	28	25.7
Size...................	norm	lighter	heavier
Diapophyses...........	norm	smallest	smaller
Diapophyses of 5th	double	single	single
Sternum.................	norm	longer	longest
Manubrium.............	norm:norm	shortest: norm	shorter: broader
Sternebrae.............	norm	shorter	longer
Xiphoid................	norm	lighter	norm
Os penis.................	absent	large	smaller
Clavicle.................	norm	longer	longer
Scapula.................	norm	shorter	longest
Caudal proc. of head...	norm	norm	heavier
Coracoid process.......	norm	norm	heavier
Humerus................	norm:norm	shorter: lighter	longer: heavier

TABLE 2—*Continued*

OSTEOLOGICAL DETAIL	HOMODONTOMYS	NEOTOMA	TEONOMA
Lesser tuberosity.......	norm	lighter	norm
Prox. medial ridge......	norm	norm	sharper
Deltoid spine...........	norm	higher	norm
Deltoid ridge...........	norm	norm	longer
Epicondylar width.....	norm	norm	broader
Ulna....................	norm	longer	shorter
Coronoid proc..........	norm	norm	sharper
Tricipital proc..........	norm	norm	sharper
Tricipital fossa.........	norm	sharper	sharper
Brachial ridge..........	norm	norm	heavier
Radius..................	norm:norm	shorter: lightest	shorter: heaviest
Falciform...............	present	present	absent
Innominate..............	norm	shorter	shorter
Femur...................	norm	norm	longer
Lesser trochanter......	norm	norm	heavier
Tibia....................	norm:norm	shorter: lighter	shortest: heavier
Semimembranous proc..	norm	norm	sharper
Popliteal fossa..........	norm	norm	deeper
Lat. tibial fossa........	norm	shallower	deeper
Groove, intern. malleol.	norm	shallower	deeper
Fibula (to notch)........	norm	longest	longer
Head...................	norm	norm	larger

Of the 62 osteological items tabled above, *Neotoma*, considered on the whole as being the subgenus which is the most intermediate in character, resembles *Homodontomys* in 21 points, *Teonoma* in 12, and is intermediate in 7. In 2 particulars does it differ from either, while in 5 it shows the greatest development and in 15 the least. These osteological variations are difficult of satisfactory interpretation for the reason that there is variation in the significance of almost every one of them. Thus a dozen variations may be of far less importance phylogenetically or adaptationally than some single other, of equally slight degree. After a careful consideration it seems probable, however, that practically all of these 22 osteological items of *Neotoma* exhibiting either greater or less development than in the other two subgenera are a result, either direct or indirect, in varying degree, of the habits and habitat predilections of that animal. On the other hand such a detail as the development of the os penis can have nothing to do with what is herein meant by life habits.

The separate items regarding bone measurements ex-

TABLE 3

TABLE OF OSTEOLOGICAL COMPARISONS EXPRESSED IN PERCENTAGES

	HOMO-DONTOMYS	NEOTOMA	TEONOMA
	per cent	*per cent*	*per cent*
Cervical vertebrae of trunk length	13.6	12.8	13.4
Thoracic vertebrae of trunk length	35.3	37.8	37.3
Lumbar vertebrae of trunk length	33.3	31.3	31.4
Sacral vertebrae of trunk length	17.7	18.0	17.9
Caudal vertebrae of trunk length	145.0	129.7	119.0
Sternum of trunk length	27.4	30.8	31.6
Clavicle of trunk length	11.9	13.0	13.0
Scapula of functional arm length	44.9	44.0	45.2
Arm (functional) of trunk length	44.4	49.3	47.1
Humerus of arm length	51.7	50.5	52.4
Ulna of arm length	58.3	60.0	57.9
Radius of ulna length	83.2	82.3	82.5
Fore foot of arm length	24.0	26.5	30.4
Innominate of leg length	46.2	45.7	45.6
Leg (functional) of trunk length	66.5	75.0	73.2
Arm (functional) of leg length	66.8	65.7	65.0
Femur of leg length	42.1	42.0	43.2
Tibia of leg length	45.0	44.5	43.1
Fibula (to notch) of tibia length	57.7	63.2	58.9
Hind foot of leg length	37.5	39.5	40.5

pressed as percentages and presented in the table above have been already discussed, but a summary is advisable. Comparison of the soft parts may show a more detailed record of adaptational specialization, did we know enough to interpret them correctly in all cases. But such information is often difficult to obtain, and in an investigation of specialization it is really to the skeleton that we must turn for most broad generalities, expressed by the relational development of the bones, one with another.

The skin muscles of the head and the platysma are best developed in *Teonoma*, indicating superior mobility of the integument of this region. Probably correlated with this are the larger vibrissae and the importance of these tactile organs in the life of this animal, while travelling the subterranean intricacies of its native rock slides. Perhaps in compensation is the fact that the panniculus carnosus, moving the body covering, is least developed in this subgenus; but why it should be heaviest in *Neotoma* is unknown.

The slight differences in the masseter superficialis as mentioned in the text but not in the tables are probably without appreciable functional difference. Due to its position, the masseter as a whole is not well situated to exhibit any variation in mass which it may have. The fact that the width of the anterior portion of the zygoma is least in *Teonoma*, and that in this subgenus the bony septum formed by the maxillary root of the zygomatic arch is smallest, indicates, however, that the masseter is weakest in that animal, slightly stronger in *Neotoma*, and strongest in *Homodontomys*. In rodents the masseter is the muscle of chief use in gnawing with the incisors, and therefore it is permissable to infer that *Homodontomys* is the one most given to such activities as piercing nuts with hard shells.

Similarly, the greater width of the posterior portion of the zygoma in *Teonoma*, coupled with its heavier temporal ridging and temporal fossae, and longer coronoid processes upon which the temporal muscles are largely inserted, indicates that the latter muscles are most powerful in this animal, less so in *Neotoma*, and least in *Homodontomys*. This is corroborated by an examination of the muscles themselves. The temporals are the muscles principally used in grinding the food with the molars, and this strengthens the contention already advanced that *Teonoma* is given to the consumption of a relatively tough, fibrous diet, *Homodontomys* of one more brittle, and *Neotoma* of a fare more intermediate in character between the two. Accessory to these facts is probably the larger pterygoideus internus of *Teonoma* and *Neotoma*, possibly slightly the best developed in the latter, as shown by the more capacious pterygoid fossae and longer angular processes of the mandible. These muscles are of use in transverse motions of the lower jaw. Of similar application is the fact that the digastricus, used to pull the jaw backwards during mastication by the molars, is largest in *Teonoma;* but the significance of the variation in the distinctness of the tendinous division of the muscle into two bellies is not known. The fossae from which arise the transversus mandibularis are, perhaps, best defined in *Teonoma* and least so in *Homodontomys*. This muscle acts to control the mobility of the symphysis menti.

The cervical vertebral series, expressed in percentage of the body length, is of approximately the same relative length in *Homodontomys* and *Teonoma*, but slightly shorter in *Neotoma*, for just what purpose can not now be stated. The inferior lamella of the sixth cervical seems if anything to be best developed in *Homodontomys* and least so in *Neotoma;* but the longus colli, which doubtless is the chief muscle influencing this process, appears to be best developed in *Teonoma*. Many of the muscles of this region exhibit subgeneric variation. The sternomastoid, cleidomastoid, scalenus, longus capitis, longus colli, splenius, complexus, and posterior portion of the biventer cervicis are all larger or longer in *Teonoma*, and most of them also in *Neotoma*, than in *Homodontomys*. The posterior portion of the biventer cervicis and the longus atlantis may be a shade the least efficient in *Teonoma*, while the rectus capitis lateralis was recorded as smaller in both *Neotoma* and *Teonoma*. These are all muscles which operate to move the head and neck, and so, on the whole, these movements should be definitely stronger in *Teonoma,* less so in *Neotoma,* and least in *Homodontomys*—for to just what purpose it is difficult to state. The omo- and stylohyoids are larger in both *Neotoma* and *Teonoma,* and the stylohyoid largest in the latter animal. These muscles help to move the hyoid bone and assist in the act of deglutition; hence we are tempted to infer that they are larger as an aid to the presumably more difficult swallowing of the more fibrous fare of *Neotoma* and *Teonoma.*

The thoracic series of vertebrae is relatively longest in *Neotoma* and but little shorter in *Teonoma.* In the lumbar series the opposite sequence is found, that of *Homodontomys* being longest, and of *Neotoma,* shortest. The subgeneric differences in the relative length of the sacral vertebrae are very slight, but they undoubtedly tell an adaptational tale had we sufficient data accumulated to understand it. The reasons causing subgeneric variation in the nine other vertebral details tabled can not be attributed to any definite muscle differences, although they have undoubtedly been caused, at least indirectly, by myological stimuli. The back muscles are always extremely complex in the precise attachments of their fibers. The only muscular differences in this region noted during dissection were that the iliocostalis, which is a lateral bender or stiffener of the back, seemed to be smaller in *Teonoma,* and the psoas minor, a vertical flexor of the lower back, was larger in both *Teonoma* and *Neotoma.*

Relative to body length the caudal series of vertebrae of *Teonoma* is 18 per cent, and of *Neotoma* 11 per cent shorter than that of *Homodontomys.* In *Teonoma* the long hairs of this member, assisted by the larger extensor caudae medialis, make up in its efficiency as a balancer for its shorter length.

Variation in the sternum, which is lightest in *Neotoma* and on the whole most robust in *Teonoma,* can not be correlated with muscular or functional facts, with any degree of certainty, as they are dependent upon both sorts of stimuli, and in addition, mechanical influence of the ribs. The sterno-fascialis, present in *Homodontomys* only, seems now to be of no definite use. The serratus posterior superior, of aid in drawing the ribs craniad, is weaker in *Neotoma* and *Teonoma*, and the sternocostalis, helping to draw the sternum forward, is smallest in the former animal and largest in the latter. Both are of use in deep breathing. The obliquus abdominis externus is a constrictor of the abdomen, and is larger in both *Neotoma* and *Teonoma*, possibly because of the increased weight of the viscera due to the more bulky fare of these two animals. This muscle acts also in holding rigid the body during extreme effort of many sorts.

The significance of the fact that the os penis is smaller in *Teonoma* than in *Neotoma*, while it is apparently absent in *Homodontomys*, is undoubtedly purely phylogenetic. In relation to body length the clavicle is slightly shorter in *Homodontomys* than in the other two subgenera, but this fact need not be dependent upon any of the muscles attached to it, for it is obvious that the length of this bone must conform to the thoracic width of the animal at this point, and the length varies with differences in body length.

The scapula, in relation to functional length of arm, is slightly shortest in *Neotoma* and longest in *Teonoma*, but the difference is too slight to be of much use to us. Of the muscles which primarily move the scapula in various directions the acromiotrapezius, levator scapulae, and serratus magnus are larger in *Teonoma* than in the other two subgenera. But the spinotrapezius was apparently weaker in both *Neotoma* and *Teonoma*, and the anterior rhomboid smallest in the former and largest in the latter. The result is undoubtedly that on the whole, scapular movements are strongest in *Teonoma*, and to all intents equal in the other two animals. The better definition of the coracoid process of *Teonoma* should indicate stronger action of the biceps brevis and coracobrachialis, originating therefrom; but no difference was noted in these muscles during dissection.

The functional length of arm in *Homodontomys* averaged 44.4, in *Neotoma* 49, and in *Teonoma* 47.5 per cent of their respective body lengths. It is unfortunate that we can not know whether this is actually due to variation in the length of the limb or of body, for there is no basic standard with which the subgeneric body lengths may be compared.

The humerus, as well as most of the bones of the extremities, is heaviest proportionate to length in *Teonoma* and lightest in *Neotoma*. It is also a trifle the longest in the former and shortest in the latter. The larger size of the humeral head in *Teonoma* is correlated only with the greater size of the bone as a whole. The teres minor is indicated as being a trifle less efficient in *Homodontomys* but this apparently has no effect upon the bone. The better definition of the proximal portion of the medial ridge in *Teonoma* seems to be due to the more triangular shape, and presumably greater strength, of the abdominal pectoral, and possibly also to slight differences in the latissimus dorsi. The deltoid spine was noted as averaging a trifle higher in *Neotoma* than the other two animals, but there seems to be no myological reason for it. In fact the acromial portion of the deltoid muscle, which might influence its height, was found to be best developed in *Teonoma*. The increased length in *Teonoma* of the deltoid ridge or rather the distinctness of its more distal portion is a reflection of the larger size in that animal of the superficial and deep pectorals acting as rotators and adductors, and the posterior division of the latter to some extent as a flexor, of the brachium. It is likely that their lever arm is slightly greater as well. Neither the lighter panniculus carnosus of this subgenus nor the heavier one of *Neotoma* seems to have caused appreciable variation at the point of insertion. The latissimus dorsi and triceps longus (flexors of the humerus) are best developed in *Teonoma*, as is the acromial portion of the deltoid, which acts chiefly as a rotator. Other rotators that are larger in this animal are the pectoral mass and teres minor—the latter larger in *Neotoma* as well. The pectorals act also as an adducting group. The fact that the epicondylar width is greater in *Teonoma* than in the other two is too complex for satisfactory analysis.

It is thus seen that the upper arm of *Teonoma* is the most powerful in practically all motions. Judging strictly from the muscles, *Neotoma* might be considered as being a trifle stronger, relative to size, than *Homodontomys*, but its lighter bone casts serious doubt upon this contention. Variations in the myology and osteology of the upper arm do not conform as nicely to our theories as those of some other parts, due, it is believed, to the complexity involved in the possible amount of movement of which this member is capable.

The relative length of the ulna in comparison with the functional length of arm is practically the same in the two more scansorial animals, although it is longer in *Neotoma*. The difference in the length of the radius is very slight, but this bone is definitely lightest in *Neotoma* and most robust in *Teonoma*. There are three ulnar details which are best developed in the latter, and a fourth more marked in this and *Neotoma* than in *Homodontomys*. The coracoid process is larger, due to a stronger joint rather than directly to any muscle; the brachial ridge is a trifle sharper, which should be attributable to increased power of either the brachialis or flexor digitorum profundus, or both, not noted during dissection; the tricipital process is larger; and the tricipital fossa is better defined in this and *Neotoma*. As no difference in the triceps medialis was discerned to account for the last two items, the variation shown by the former at least is probably ascribable to a stronger joint. The epitrochlearis and triceps longus, which act as extensors of the forearm,